C000243367

**Mathematics Enhancement P**

**Demonstration Project**

# Practice Book: Y8A

*Principal Author:* Ted Graham, Centre for Teaching Mathematics, Plymouth University

*Senior Editor:* David Burghes, Centre for Innovation in Mathematics Teaching

*Advisors:*

| | |
|---|---|
| Graham Bryant | Caldicot Comprehensive School, Monmouthshire |
| Chris Graddon | Streetly School, Sutton Coldfield, West Midlands |
| Chris Hall | Hassenbrook School, Stanford-le-Hope, Essex |
| Malcolm Jenkin | Penair School, Truro, Cornwall |
| Mary Ledwick | Our Lady and St John High School, Blackburn |
| Graham Middleton | Stanchester Community School, Stoke-sub-Hamdon, Somerset |
| Adrian Smith | Penair School, Truro, Cornwall |

*Typesetter:* Liz Holland

*Checkers:* Nigel Oates, Albine Patterson

This is one component of MEP Mathematics resources for Y8.

All enquiries regarding these resources should be addressed to

Mathematics Enhancement Programme
CIMT, Institute of Education
Plymouth University          Tel:   01752 585346
Plymouth  PL4 8AA           Fax:   01752 586520

First Printed     August 1999

Design by *Clinton Banbury*
P.O. Box 2892, Billericay, Essex  CM11  2LF
Tel:    01277 630421

# Contents

# 1 Mathematical Diagrams

## 1.1 Mileage Charts

In this section we look at mileage charts.

### Example 1

Distances in the table below are given in miles.

|       |        |        |          |          |         |
|-------|--------|--------|----------|----------|---------|
| 100   | BRISTOL |       |          |          |         |
| 55    | 84     | EXETER |          |          |         |
| 108   | 194    | 110    | PENZANCE |          |         |
| 67    | 125    | 44     | 77       | PLYMOUTH |         |
| 50    | 51     | 34     | 144      | 75       | TAUNTON |

(BARNSTAPLE heads the first column)

Using the table, answer the following questions:

(a)   How far is it from Taunton to Exeter?

(b)   Jerry travels from Barnstaple to Exeter, then from Exeter to Plymouth, and finally from Plymouth back to Barnstaple.
      How far does he travel altogether?

### Solution

(a)   34 miles (see table and diagram opposite).

(b)   Barnstaple to Exeter:        55 miles

      Exeter to Plymouth:          44 miles

      Plymouth to Barnstaple:  67 miles

      Total distance = 55 + 44 + 67

                     = 166 miles

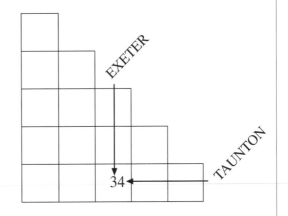

## Example 2

The network diagram opposite shows the distances, in miles, between some towns.

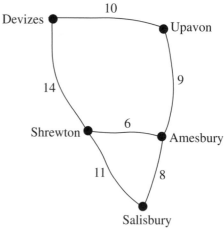

Copy and complete the following mileage chart to show the shortest distances between these towns:

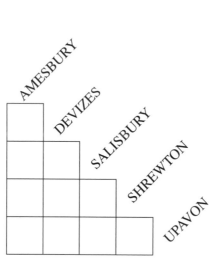

## Solution

The direct distances can be completed first:

the shortest route from Amesbury to Devizes is via Upavon, a total of 19 miles;

the shortest route from Devizes to Salisbury is via Shrewton, a total of 25 miles;

the shortest route from Salisbury to Upavon is via Amesbury, a total of 17 miles;

the shortest route from Shrewton to Upavon is via Amesbury, a total of 15 miles.

With this information, the table can now be completed, as shown opposite.

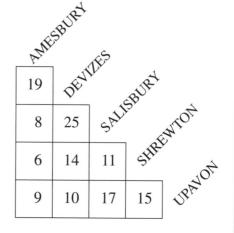

## Exercises

1. Use the table opposite, where the distances are given in miles, to find out how far it is from:

   (a) Leeds to Lincoln,

   (b) Hull to York,

   (c) Leeds to Manchester,

   (d) Sheffield to Leeds,

   (e) Manchester to York.

| HULL | LEEDS | LINCOLN | MANCHESTER | SHEFFIELD | YORK |
|------|-------|---------|------------|-----------|------|
| 60 | | | | | |
| 47 | 72 | | | | |
| 97 | 44 | 85 | | | |
| 66 | 36 | 47 | 39 | | |
| 38 | 24 | 80 | 71 | 57 | |

2. Ross travels from Leeds to Manchester, then from Manchester to Sheffield and finally from Sheffield back to Leeds. Use the table in question 1 to calculate the total distance he travels.

3. Hannah drives from Bristol to Exeter, continues to Plymouth, on to Barnstaple and from there back to Bristol. Use the table in Example 1 to calculate the total distance she drives.

4. The table opposite gives the distances in kilometres between some towns in northern France.

   What is the distance between:

   (a) Alençon and Paris,

   (b) Reims and Orleans,

   (c) Rouen and Calais,

   (d) Paris and Reims,

   (e) Le Mans and Rouen?

| ALENÇON | CALAIS | LE MANS | ORLEANS | PARIS | REIMS | ROUEN |
|---------|--------|---------|---------|-------|-------|-------|
| 365 | | | | | | |
| 49 | 419 | | | | | |
| 167 | 433 | 138 | | | | |
| 220 | 293 | 204 | 135 | | | |
| 355 | 278 | 340 | 270 | 146 | | |
| 146 | 215 | 199 | 210 | 140 | 284 | |

5. Debbie drives from Calais to Paris and back while she is on holiday. Use the table in question 4 to calculate how far she travels altogether on this journey.

6. Laura travels from Calais to Paris, on to Alençon and then to Rouen before returning to Paris. Use the table in question 4 to calculate how far she travels altogether.

7.    The diagram below shows the distances, in miles, between some junctions
      on the M2 motorway:

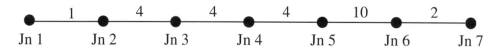

      Copy and complete the chart below to show the shortest distances between
      junctions:

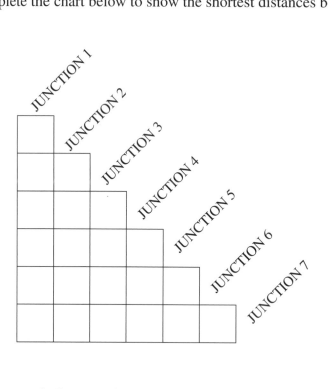

8.    The following network diagram shows the distances, in miles, between
      some towns in Wales:

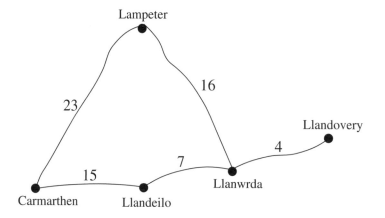

      Use the information in the diagram to complete a copy of the table on the
      next page, giving the shortest distances between the towns.

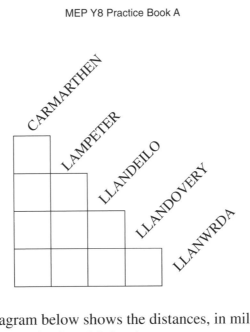

9.    The network diagram below shows the distances, in miles, by road between
      some towns close to the Scottish border:

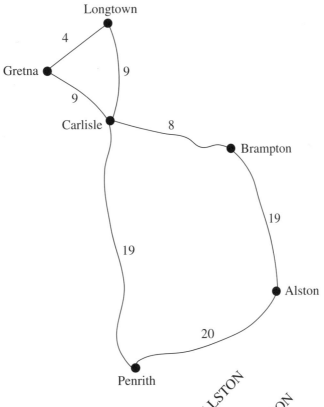

Use information from the diagram
to complete a copy of the table
opposite, giving the shortest
distances between the towns.

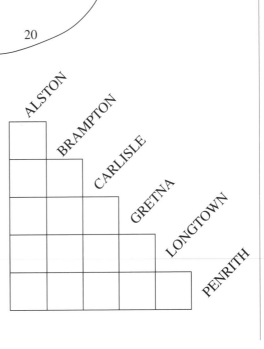

10.   The diagram below shows stations on the GNER railway:

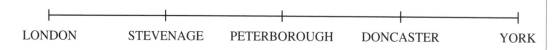

LONDON        STEVENAGE    PETERBOROUGH      DONCASTER            YORK

Some distances, in miles, are shown
in the table opposite.

(a)    Copy the table and fill in
       the missing distances.

(b)    What distance is travelled
       in a return journey between
       London and York?

| LONDON | STEVENAGE | PETERBOROUGH | DONCASTER | YORK |
|---|---|---|---|---|
| 21 | | | | |
| 68 | 47 | | | |
| 188 | 167 | 120 | | |
| | | | 45 | |

## 1.2  Using Flow Charts to Plan Practical Tasks

A flow chart can be used to organise the instructions for carrying out a task.
Boxes of different shapes are used for particular operations:

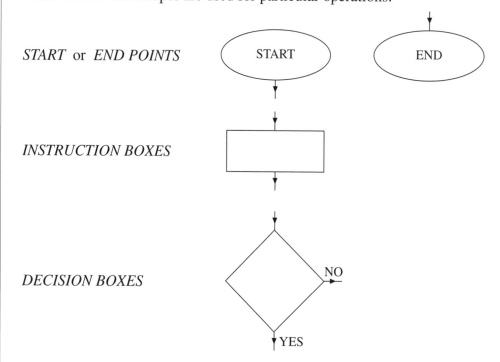

*START* or *END POINTS*

*INSTRUCTION BOXES*

*DECISION BOXES*

Each box contains only *one* instruction.

## Example 1

Draw a flow chart to give the instructions for making a mug of tea.

## Solution

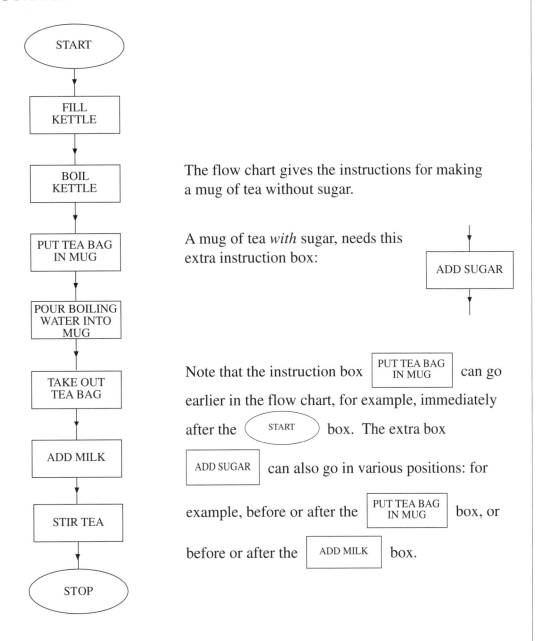

The flow chart gives the instructions for making a mug of tea without sugar.

A mug of tea *with* sugar, needs this extra instruction box:

Note that the instruction box [PUT TEA BAG IN MUG] can go earlier in the flow chart, for example, immediately after the (START) box. The extra box

[ADD SUGAR] can also go in various positions: for example, before or after the [PUT TEA BAG IN MUG] box, or

before or after the [ADD MILK] box.

## Example 2

The instruction [BOIL KETTLE] in Example 1 can be broken down into separate stages.

Draw a flow chart to show this.

## Solution

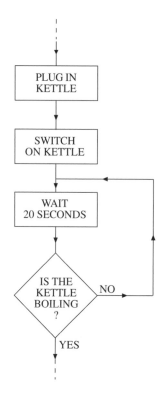

## Example 3

Draw a flow chart showing how to find a programme you would like to watch on television.

## Solution

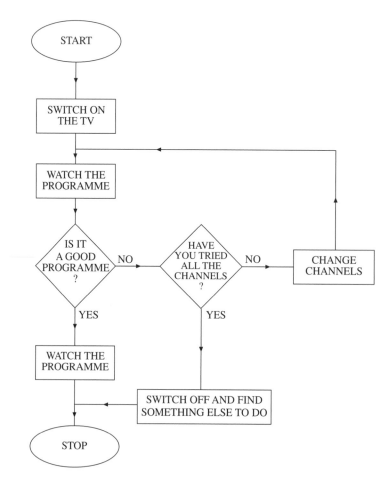

# Exercises

1.  Draw a flow chart showing how to prepare a drink of blackcurrant squash in a glass.

2.  Draw a flow chart for each of the following:

    (a)  making a cup of coffee with milk and sugar,

    (b)  buying a can of drink from a vending machine,

    (c)  making a telephone call from a pay phone,

    (d)  shutting down a computer.

3.  Draw a flow chart that describes how to cross a road. You should include decision boxes in your flow chart.

4.  Imagine you are driving along a road. You see a 30 mph speed limit sign and a speed camera. Draw a flow chart that you, as a sensible driver, would be advised to follow.

5.  Jerry needs to work out $4.72 \times 11.61$ using a calculator.

    (a)  Draw a flow chart to show how to carry out this calculation on a calculator.

    (b)  Redraw the flow chart to include all the following processes:

         (i)   *estimating* the answer to $4.72 \times 11.61$,

         (ii)  *calculating* the answer to $4.72 \times 11.61$

         (iii) comparing the answer with the estimate to decide whether the calculator answer is reasonable.

6.  You are playing *Snakes and Ladders*.

    (a)  Draw a flow chart to describe how to move your counter for one go.

    (b)  Describe how you would change your chart when you have an extra turn after throwing a six.

# 1.3 Using a Flow Chart for Classification

Flow charts can also be used to sort or classify things.

## Example 1

This flow chart can be used to classify angles between 0 ° and 360 °. What comes out at the end points A, B, C, D and E ?

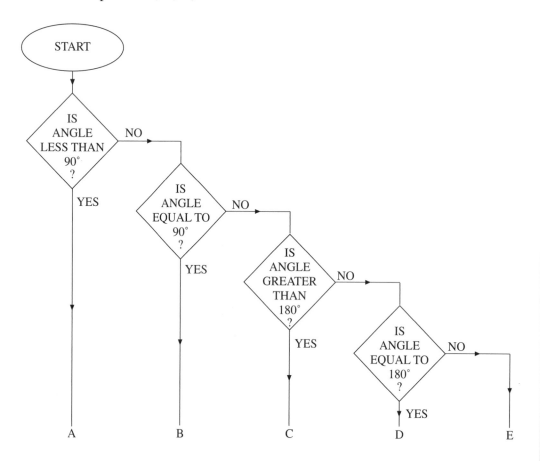

## Solution

A   Angles less than 90 °                          ACUTE ANGLES

B   Angles equal to 90 °                           RIGHT ANGLES

C   Angles greater than 180 °                      REFLEX ANGLES

D   Angles equal to 180 °              ANGLES ON STRAIGHT LINES

E   Angles greater than 90 ° but less than 180 °    OBTUSE ANGLES

## Example 2

The flow chart below can be used for sorting quadrilaterals:

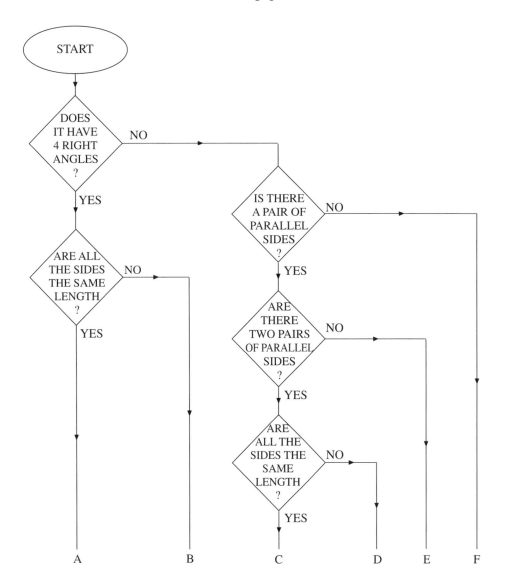

Where would each of these shapes come out?

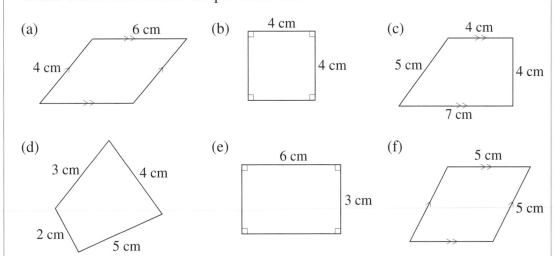

## Solution

(a)    A parallelogram;  comes out at D.

(b)    A square;  comes out at A.

(c)    A trapezium;  comes out at E.

(d)    Quadrilateral with no special properties;  comes out at F.

(e)    A rectangle;  comes out at B.

(f)    A rhombus;  comes out at C.

## Exercises

1.    The angles below are classified using the flow chart in Example 1.  Where
      does each angle come out of the flow chart?

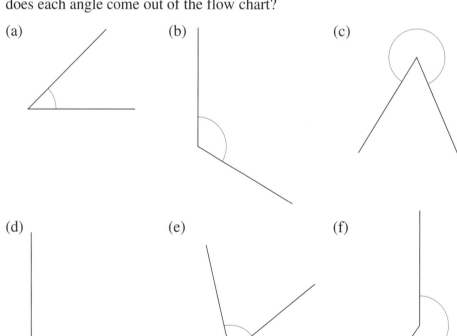

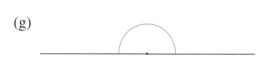

2.    The quadrilaterals below can be classified using the flow chart in
      Example 2. Where does each quadrilateral come out of the flow chart?

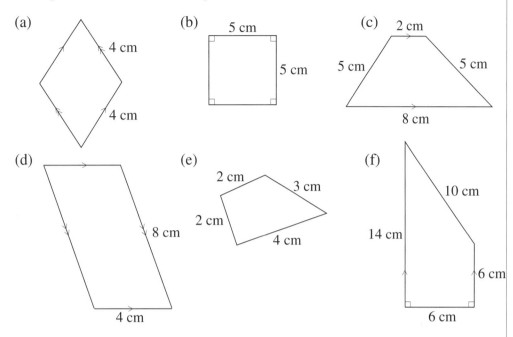

(a)    4 cm    4 cm

(b)    5 cm    5 cm

(c)    2 cm    5 cm    5 cm    8 cm

(d)    8 cm    4 cm

(e)    2 cm    3 cm    2 cm    4 cm

(f)    10 cm    14 cm    6 cm    6 cm

3.    Draw a flow chart that will sort trees, into those that shed their leaves
      during winter, and those that do not.

4.    Draw a flow chart that will sort triangles into *equilateral* (all sides of equal
      length), *isosceles* (two sides of equal length) or *scalene* (all sides of
      different lengths).

5.    Draw a flow chart that will sort polygons into the following categories:

         *Triangles*

         *Quadrilaterals*

         *Pentagons*

         *Hexagons*

         *Heptagons*

         *Octagons*

         *Polygons with more than 8 sides*

6.    The flow chart on the following page can be used to sort animals.

      (a)    Where would each of these animals come out of the flow chart?

         *Monkey*              *Bird*                *Giraffe*

         *Horse*               *Centipede*           *Elephant*

         *Zebra*               *Pig*                 *Kangaroo*

         *Fish*                *Dolphin*             *Cat*

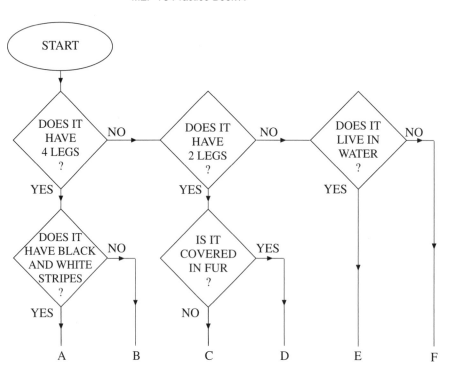

(b)    Name one more animal that would come out of the flow chart at each of the end points A, B, C, D and E.

7.    The following flow chart will sort numbers. The numbers 1 to 10 are put into this flow chart. Where do they each come out?

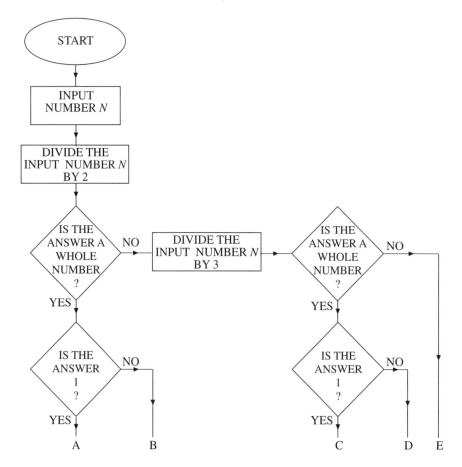

8.    Draw a flow chart that will classify numbers as *odd* or *even*.

9.    Draw a flow chart that will test numbers up to 20 to see if they are prime.

# 1.4  Networks

In this section we consider networks.  Problems can be solved by finding the shortest or quickest route through a network, which can represent a system of roads, pipelines, cables, or anything else that connects different points or places.

## Example 1

Find the shortest route from A to G, using the distances shown on the network opposite:

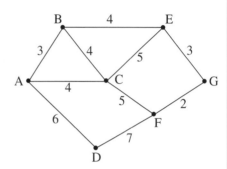

## Solution

First find the shortest distances from A to the points B, C and D; these are shown in circles on this diagram:

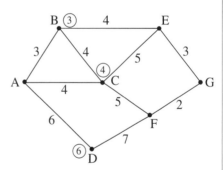

Now work out the shortest distances from A to E and F and put these in circles on the diagram:

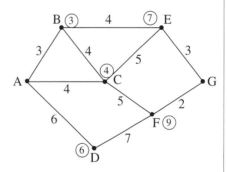

It is now possible to see that the shortest route from A to G is 10, using the route, A B E G.

## Example 2

Find the shortest route from S to T through this network:

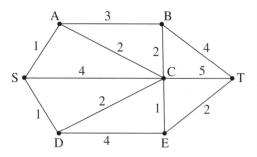

## Solution

The diagram opposite shows the shortest routes from S to A, C and D:

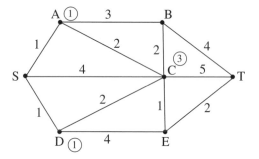

The shortest routes from S to B and E are now added to the diagram:

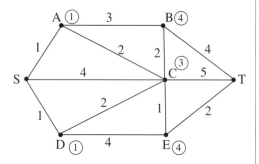

We can see that the shortest route from S to T is 6, using either route  S D C E T  or route  S A C E T.

# Exercises

1. The network diagram below shows the distances between some towns and cities:

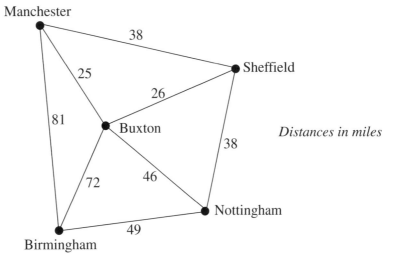

*Distances in miles*

Find the shortest distance and route between:

(a) Manchester and Nottingham,

(b) Sheffield and Birmingham.

2. The diagram below shows the shortest journey times, in hours, between 5 towns, A, B, C, S and T:

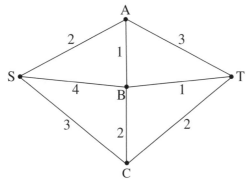

Find the shortest journey time from S to T and state the route.

3. The network diagram below shows the distances between some towns and cities in the south west of England:

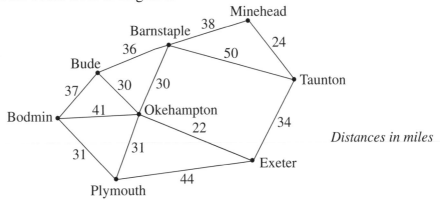

*Distances in miles*

17

Find the shortest distance and route between:

(a) Bodmin and Exeter,

(b) Plymouth and Minehead.

4. The network diagram below shows some of the places on the Isle of Man, and the distances between them:

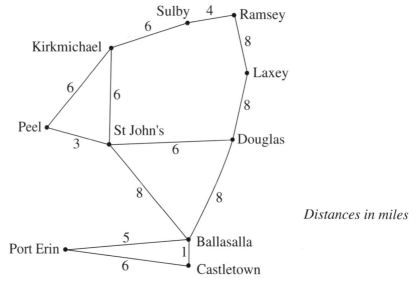

*Distances in miles*

Which is the shortest route and what is the distance from:

(a) Douglas to Sulby,

(b) Ramsey to Port Erin,

(c) Peel to Laxey?

5. Use the network diagram below to find both the shortest route and the distance from Carlisle to Lincoln.

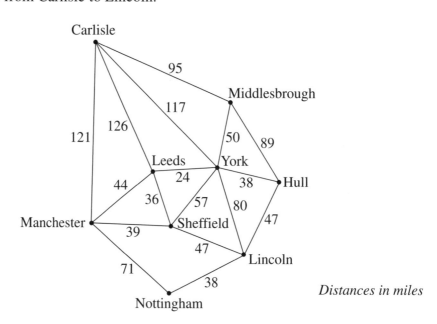

*Distances in miles*

# 1.5 Critical Path Analysis

When you are planning to carry out a task, critical path analysis can be used to help you find the most efficient way to do it; this works by showing how activities need to be scheduled.

For example, when making your breakfast, you can boil the kettle *and* cook your toast at the same time. You do not have to wait until you have boiled the kettle before you start to make your toast, whereas you *do* have to boil the kettle before you can make a cup of tea.

## Example 1

Veronica is going to make a cake. She has six tasks to do, which are listed below:

| | Activity | Time needed in minutes | Preceded by |
|---|---|---|---|
| A | Warm oven | 15 | |
| B | Weigh ingredients | 3 | |
| C | Mix ingredients | 5 | Weigh ingredients |
| D | Bake cake | 20 | Mix ingredients |
| E | Wash up mixing bowl and utensils | 8 | Mix ingredients |
| F | Wash up cake tin | 2 | Bake cake |

Draw an activity network and find the shortest time to make the cake.

## Solution

The first step is to draw an *activity network*, which is a way of showing the data concerning the tasks that have to be completed, how long each one takes, and the order in which they must be undertaken. The activity network for making Veronica's cake is shown below:

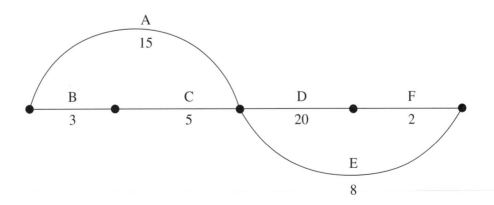

We move through the network from *left to right,* calculating the earliest start time for each activity. For example, D (bake cake) cannot begin until A, B and C have all happened, i.e. the oven is warm and the cake ingredients have been weighed out and mixed. The oven requires at least 15 minutes to warm, so the earliest time that D and E can start is 15 minutes after warming the oven. In turn, this means that F cannot start until 35 minutes have elapsed.

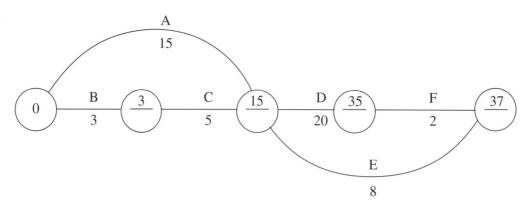

At this stage, we can see that the shortest time to complete the task of baking the cake is 37 minutes.

We then work through the network from *right to left,* calculating the latest start time for each activity. For example, E could begin 29 minutes after the start, and still finish at the same time as F. However, D must begin no later than 15 minutes after the start, for the whole activity to be completed in 37 minutes.

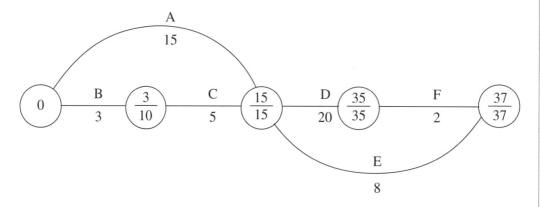

The *critical path* is A D F as these tasks must be completed on time or the whole project will be delayed.

For activity E there is a *float time* of 14 minutes. We use this term because there is a 22 minute period in which the activity must take place, but the task itself takes only 8 minutes. C also has a float time, but this time of 7 minutes duration.

There is *no float time* for tasks on the critical path.

## Example 2

On the following activity network the numbers show the time, in minutes, for each task. Complete the earliest and latest finishing times for each task, identify the critical path, and state the shortest completion time for the whole activity.

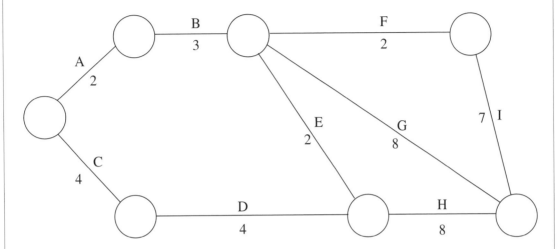

## Solution

The layout of the activity network, from left to right, tells us the following information about the order in which the tasks must be carried out:

| Task | Time (minutes) | Preceded by |
|:---:|:---:|:---|
| A | 2 | |
| B | 3 | A |
| C | 4 | |
| D | 4 | C |
| E | 2 | A, B |
| F | 2 | A, B |
| G | 8 | A, B |
| H | 8 | A, B, C, D, E |
| I | 7 | A, B, F |

We first calculate the earliest start time for each activity by working from *left to right* through the activity network:

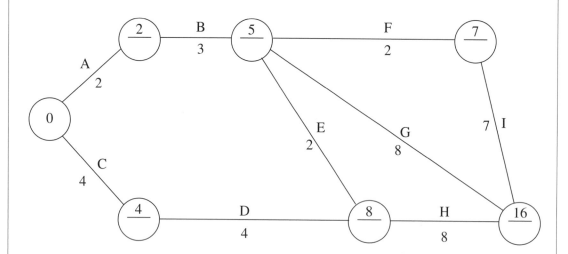

We now work back from *right to left,* calculating the latest start time for each activity:

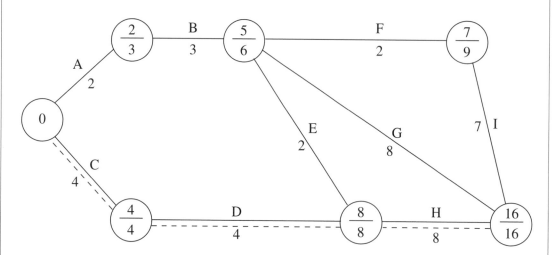

So the critical path is  C D H,  because for this route the earliest start times match the latest start times.

The shortest completion time is 16 minutes.

The diagram shows that there are float times for some activities; for example, 2 minutes for activity I, and 1 minute for both activities F and B.

## Example 3

The table lists the tasks needed to completely refurbish a kitchen; the times are given in days. Find both the critical path, and the shortest completion time.

| | Task | Time needed | Preceded by |
|---|---|---|---|
| A | Design kitchen | 8 | |
| B | Make kitchen units | 11 | A |
| C | Remove old units | 2 | A |
| D | Fit new power points | 1 | C |
| E | Fit new plumbing | 2 | C |
| F | Paint and decorate | 3 | D, E |
| G | Fit new units | 5 | B, F |
| H | Fix wall tiles | 3 | G |

## Solution

The activity network is shown below:

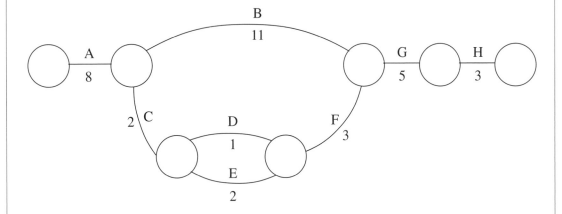

Now move from left to right through the network to find the earliest start times:

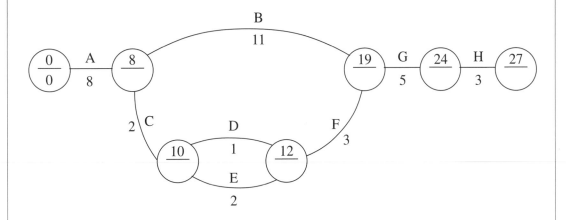

23

Now work back through the network, putting in the latest start times:

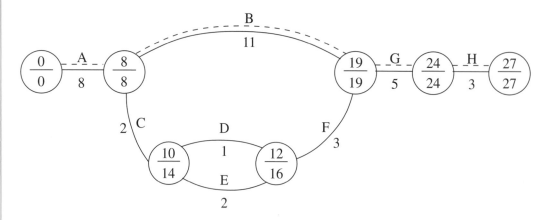

The critical path is A B G H, as shown in the diagram, and the shortest completion time is 27 days.

# Exercises

1. The activity diagram below shows the time, in minutes, for different parts of a process. Find the critical path and the shortest possible completion time.

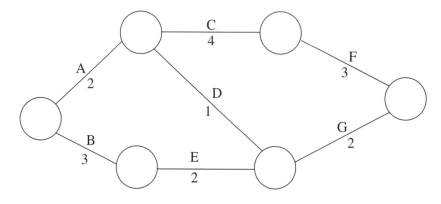

2. Jamil and Halim are making a model garage for their brother's birthday present.

   There are a number of tasks that must be completed to make the garage; these are listed in the table opposite:

| | Task | Time needed (hours) |
|---|---|---|
| A | Design the garage | 1 |
| B | Buy materials | 2 |
| C | Cut out wooden panels | 2 |
| D | Glue panels in place | 1 |
| E | Paint garage | 2 |
| F | Make cars | 3 |
| G | Paint cars | 3 |

The activity network is shown below:

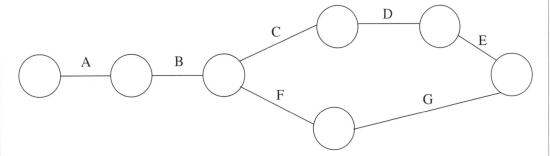

Find the critical path and the shortest possible completion time.

3. The following instructions must be carried out to put up a dome tent:

| | *Task* | *Time (mins)* | *Preceded by* |
|---|---|---|---|
| A | Peg down inner tent | 3 | |
| B | Assemble poles | 1 | |
| C | Fit poles in flysheet | 4 | B |
| D | Erect flysheet | 4 | A, B, C |
| E | Peg down flysheet | 2 | A, B, C, D |
| F | Hang inner tent from poles | 2 | A, B, C, D |
| G | Attach guy ropes | 4 | A, B, C, D, E |

The activity network is shown below:

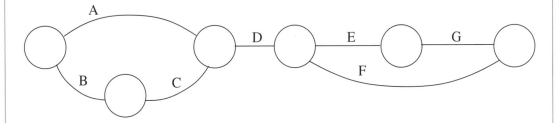

Find both the critical path, and the shortest time needed to put up the tent.

4. You are going to prepare a meal of chicken and potato pie, peas and gravy. You have to carry out the tasks listed below:

| | Task | Time (mins) | Preceded by |
|---|---|---|---|
| A | Peel potatoes | 10 | |
| B | Heat oven | 5 | |
| C | Make pie | 12 | A |
| D | Cook pie | 40 | B,  C |
| E | Make gravy | 5 | B,  C |
| F | Cook peas | 8 | B,  C |
| G | Cook potatoes | 25 | A |
| H | Lay table | 2 | |

(a) Draw an activity network in line with the information given in the table.

(b) Find both the critical path and the shortest time needed to prepare the meal.

(c) Which tasks have a float time? State the float times for these activities.

5. The building of a house is broken down into the tasks listed in the table below. Draw a network diagram and use it to find the critical path and the shortest possible construction time.

| | Task | Time (days) | Preceded by |
|---|---|---|---|
| A | Order materials | 5 | |
| B | Lay drains | 7 | A |
| C | Lay foundations | 7 | B |
| D | Erect blockwork | 11 | C |
| E | Roofing work | 5 | D |
| F | Install floors | 4 | E |
| G | Plumbing and heating | 10 | F |
| H | Electrical installation | 6 | F |
| I | Install windows | 5 | D |
| J | Plastering | 6 | G,  H,  I |
| K | Decoration | 5 | J |
| L | Install fittings | 3 | K |
| M | Clear site | 2 | L |
| N | Lay paths | 2 | D |

# 2 Factors

## 2.1 Factors and Prime Numbers

A *factor* divides *exactly* into a number, leaving *no* remainder. For example, 13 is a *factor* of 26 because $26 \div 13 = 2$ leaving no remainder.

A *prime number* has only *two* factors, 1 and itself; this is how a prime number is defined.

5 is a prime number because it has only two factors, 1 and 5.

8 has factors 1, 2, 4 and 8, so it is *not* prime.

1 is *not* a prime number because it has only one factor, namely 1 itself.

### Example 1

(a) List the factors of the numbers 1, 2, 3, 4, 5, 6, 7, 8, 9 and 10.

(b) Which of these numbers are *prime* numbers?

### Solution

(a) This table lists the factors of these numbers:

| Number | Factors |
|--------|---------|
| 1 | 1 |
| 2 | 1, 2 |
| 3 | 1, 3 |
| 4 | 1, 2, 4 |
| 5 | 1, 5 |
| 6 | 1, 2, 3, 6 |
| 7 | 1, 7 |
| 8 | 1, 2, 4, 8 |
| 9 | 1, 3, 9 |
| 10 | 1, 2, 5, 10 |

(b) The numbers 2, 3, 5 and 7 have exactly two factors, and so only they are prime numbers.

## Example 2

List the prime factors of 24.

## Solution

First list all the factors of 24, and they are:

$$1, \ 2, \ 3, \ 4, \ 6, \ 8, \ 12, \ 24$$

Now select from this list the numbers that are prime; these are 2 and 3, and so the prime factors of 24 are 2 and 3.

## Example 3

Which of the following numbers are prime numbers:

$$18, \quad 45, \quad 79 \quad \text{and} \quad 90 ?$$

## Solution

The factors of 18 are 1, 2, 3, 6, 9 and 18;  18 is not a prime number.

The factors of 45 are 1, 3, 5, 9, 15 and 45;  45 is not a prime number.

The factors of 79 are 1 and 79;  79 is a prime number

The factors of 90 are 1, 2, 3, 5, 6, 9, 10, 15, 18, 30, 45 and 90;  90 is not a prime number.

79 is the only prime number in the list.

---

*Divisibility Test*

If a number is divisible by **2**, it will end with 0, 2, 4, 6 or 8.

If a number is divisible by **3**, the *sum* of its digits will be a multiple of 3.

If a number is divisible by **4**, the last two digits will be a multiple of 4.

If a number is divisible by **5**, it will end in 0 or 5.

If a number is divisible by **9**, the *sum* of its digits will be a multiple of 9.

If a number is divisible by **10**, it will end in 0.

*Can you find tests for divisibility by other numbers?*

---

## Exercises

1. (a) List all the factors of each of the following numbers:

   11, 12, 13, 14, 15, 16, 17, 18, 19, 20

   (b) Which of these numbers are prime?

2. Explain why 99 is *not* a prime number.

3. Which of the following are prime numbers:

   33, 35, 37, 39 ?

4. Find the prime factors of 72.

5. (a) Find the prime factors of 40.

   (b) Find the prime factors of 70.

   (c) Which prime factors do 40 and 70 have in common?

6. Find the prime factors that 48 and 54 have in common.

7. A number has prime factors 2, 5 and 7. Which is the *smallest* number that has these prime factors?

8. The first 5 prime numbers are 2, 3, 5, 7 and 11. Which is the *smallest* number that has these prime factors?

9. Write down the first *two* prime numbers which are greater than 100.

10. Which is the first prime number that is greater than 200?

## 2.2 Prime Factors

A *factor tree* may be used to help find the prime factors of a number.

### Example 1

Draw a factor tree for the number 36.

### Solution

Start with 36 and then:

split 36 into numbers 9 and 4 that multiply to give 36 as shown in the factor tree opposite;

repeat for the 9 and the 4, as shown on the factor tree.

The factor tree is now complete because the numbers at the ends of the branches are prime numbers; the prime numbers have been ringed.

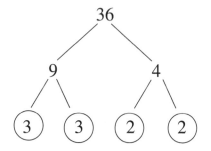

Another possible factor tree for 36 is shown here:

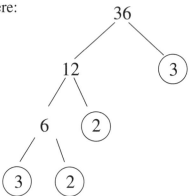

> On the factor tree we only put a ring around the prime numbers.

Note that, at the end of the branches, both the numbers 2 and 3 appear twice.

The prime factors of 36 are 3, 2, 2 and 3.

In ascending order, the prime factors of 36 are 2, 2, 3, 3.

---

From the factor trees above it is possible to write:

$$36 = 2 \times 2 \times 3 \times 3$$
$$= 2^2 \times 3^2$$

When a number is written in this way, it is said to be written as the *product of its prime factors*.

---

## Example 2

Express each of the following numbers as the product of its prime factors:

(a)    102                    (b)    60

## Solution

(a)    Start by creating a factor tree:

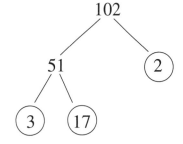

$102 = 2 \times 3 \times 17$

(b)    Start by creating a factor tree:

$60 = 5 \times 3 \times 2 \times 2$

Put the prime numbers in ascending order:

$60 = 2 \times 2 \times 3 \times 5$

$\phantom{60} = 2^2 \times 3 \times 5$

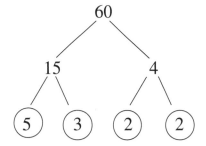

## Example 3

A number is expressed as the product of its prime factors as

$2^3 \times 3^2 \times 5$

What is the number?

## Solution

$2^3 \times 3^2 \times 5 = 2 \times 2 \times 2 \times 3 \times 3 \times 5$

$\phantom{2^3 \times 3^2 \times 5} = 360$

## Exercises

1.   Draw factor trees for the following numbers:

    (a)   20              (b)   100            (c)   88

2.   Draw two different factor trees for 40.

3.   (a)   Draw two different factor trees for 66.

    (b)   Can you draw any other different factor trees for 66?

4.   Copy the factor tree opposite and fill in the missing numbers:

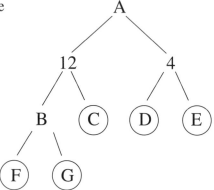

5.   Fill in the missing numbers on a copy of the factor tree opposite:

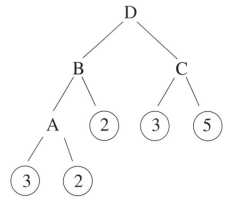

6.   Use a factor tree to find the prime factors of:

    (a)   30              (b)   80            (c)   200

7.   Write each of the following numbers as the product of their prime factors:

    (a)   62              (b)   64            (c)   82

    (d)   320           (e)   90            (f)   120

    (g)   54              (h)   38            (i)   1000

8.   A number is expressed as the product of its prime factors as:

$$2^3 \times 3 \times 5^2$$

What is the number?

9. The prime factors of a number are 2, 7 and 11.

   Which are the three *smallest* numbers with these prime factors?

10. Which is the *smallest* number that has:

    (a) 4 different prime factors,

    (b) 5 prime factors?

11. (a) Write down two numbers, neither of which must end in 0, and which multiply together to give 1000.

    (b) Repeat question 11 (a), this time writing down two numbers which multiply to give 1 000 000.

# 2.3 Index Notation

You will have seen the occasional use of index notation in the last section; for example, in the statement

$$2^3 \times 3^2 \times 5 = 360$$

which contains 2 indices.

We read $2^3$ as *"two to the power of three"* or *"two cubed"*: 2 is the *base number*, 3 is the *index*.

In general, $a^n$ is the result of multiplying the base number, $a$, by itself $n$ times, $n$ being the index.

$$a^n = a \times a \times a \times \ldots\ldots\ldots \times a \times a \times a \times a$$
$$\xleftarrow{\hspace{2cm}} n \text{ times} \xrightarrow{\hspace{2cm}}$$

A calculator can be used to work out powers. The index button is usually marked $x^y$ or $y^x$. Sometimes you will need to press the SHIFT or 2nd FUNCTION key before using the index button. You should find out which buttons you need to use on your calculator.

For example, to calculate $5^4$ you may need to press

       either     ⑤ $\boxed{x^y}$ ④ $\boxed{=}$

       or     ⑤ $\boxed{\text{SHIFT}}$ $\boxed{\;}^{x^y}$ ④ $\boxed{=}$

to get the correct answer of 625.

## Example 1

Calculate:

(a)   $2^4$                     (b)   $7^3$                     (c)   $10^5$

Check your answers using a calculator.

## Solution

(a)   $2^4$  $=$  $2 \times 2 \times 2 \times 2$

       $=$  $16$

Using a calculator,

either   $\boxed{2}$  $\boxed{\text{SHIFT}}$  $\overset{x^y}{\boxed{\phantom{0}}}$  $\boxed{4}$  $\boxed{=}$  16

or   $\boxed{2}$  $\boxed{x^y}$  $\boxed{4}$  $\boxed{=}$  16

(b)   $7^3$  $=$  $7 \times 7 \times 7$

       $=$  $343$

Using a calculator,

either   $\boxed{7}$  $\boxed{\text{SHIFT}}$  $\overset{x^y}{\boxed{\phantom{0}}}$  $\boxed{3}$  $\boxed{=}$  343

or   $\boxed{7}$  $\boxed{x^y}$  $\boxed{3}$  $\boxed{=}$  343

(c)   $10^5$  $=$  $10 \times 10 \times 10 \times 10 \times 10$

       $=$  $100\ 000$

Using a calculator,

either   $\boxed{1}$  $\boxed{0}$  $\boxed{\text{SHIFT}}$  $\overset{x^y}{\boxed{\phantom{0}}}$  $\boxed{5}$  $\boxed{=}$  100 000

or   $\boxed{1}$  $\boxed{0}$  $\boxed{x^y}$  $\boxed{5}$  $\boxed{=}$  100 000

## Example 2

Write these statements, filling in the missing numbers:

(a)   $32 = 2^{\square}$                     (b)   $1000000 = 10^{\square}$

## Solution

(a)   $32$  $=$  $2 \times 2 \times 2 \times 2 \times 2$

       $=$  $2^5$

(b)   $1\ 000\ 000$  $=$  $10 \times 10 \times 10 \times 10 \times 10 \times 10$

            $=$  $10^6$

**Exercises**

1.   Copy the following statements and fill in the missing numbers:

   (a)   $6 \times 6 \times 6 \times 6 \times 6 = 6^{\square}$

   (b)   $3 \times 3 \times 3 \times 3 = 3^{\square}$

   (c)   $7 \times 7 \times 7 \times 7 \times 7 \times 7 = 7^{\square}$

   (d)   $9 \times 9 \times 9 \times 9 \times 9 = 9^{\square}$

2.   Calculate:

   (a)   $2^3$

   (b)   $3^3$

   (c)   $10^4$

   (d)   $5^3$

   (e)   $2^7$

   (f)   $3^4$

   (g)   $9^2$

   (h)   $10^3$

   (i)   $10^7$

3.   Copy the following statements and fill in the missing numbers:

   (a)   $100 = 10^{\square}$

   (b)   $81 = \square^2$

   (c)   $81 = \square^4$

   (d)   $16 = \square^4$

   (e)   $16 = \square^2$

   (f)   $7^{\square} = 2401$

4.   Calculate:

   (a)   $5^2 \times 2^2$

   (b)   $3^2 \times 2^4$

   (c)   $7^2 \times 2^3$

   (d)   $6^2 \times 2$

   (e)   $9^2 \times 3$

   (f)   $5^3 \times 2^3$

5.   Copy each of the following statements and fill in the missing numbers:

   (a)   $2^3 \times 2^5 = (2 \times 2 \times 2) \times (2 \times 2 \times 2 \times 2 \times 2)$

   $= 2 \times 2 \times 2 \times 2 \times 2 \times 2 \times 2 \times 2$

   $= 2^{\square}$

   (b)   $5^7 \times 5^2 = (5 \times 5 \times 5 \times 5 \times 5 \times 5 \times 5) \times (5 \times 5)$

   $= 5 \times 5 \times 5 \times 5 \times 5 \times 5 \times 5 \times 5 \times 5$

   $= 5^{\square}$

   (c)   $6^4 \times 6^2 = 6^{\square}$

   (d)   $7^3 \times 7^7 = 7^{\square}$

   (e)   $8^6 \times 8 = 8^{\square}$

6.   Copy the following statements and fill in the missing numbers:

(a)   $9^3 = 9 \times 9 \times 9$

$= (3 \times 3) \times (3 \times 3) \times (3 \times 3)$

$= 3 \times 3 \times 3 \times 3 \times 3 \times 3$

$= 3^{\square}$

(b)   $9^4 = 3^{\square}$

7.   If $4^2 = 2^n$, which number does $n$ represent?  Answer this question using a similar method to the one used in question 6.

8.   If $4^n = 2^{12}$, which number does $n$ represent?

9.   If $125^4 = 5^n$, which number does $n$ represent?

10.  Copy the following statements and fill in the missing numbers:

(a)   $5^4 \times 2^4 = 10^{\square}$                    (b)   $3^5 \times 2^5 = 6^{\square}$

(c)   $4^{\square} \times 2^3 = 8^3$                      (d)   $7^5 \times 3^5 = 21^{\square}$

(e)   $7^4 \times \square^4 = 28^4$                      (f)   $5^9 \times \square^9 = 10^9$

# 2.4  Highest Common Factor and Lowest Common Multiple

> The *highest common factor* (HCF) of two numbers is the largest number that is a factor of both.

The factors of 12 are  1,   2,  ③,  4,   6,   12.
The factors of 15 are  1, ③  5,   15.

So the HCF of 12 and 15 is 3.

The HCF is easy to find for some numbers, but for others it is more difficult.  In harder cases, the best way to find the HCF is to use prime factors.

## Example 1

Find the HCF of:

(a)    20 and 30                          (b)    14 and 12

## Solution

(a)    The factors of  20  are    1,    2,    4,    5,  ⑩  and  20.

   The factors of  30  are    1,    2,    3,    5,    6,  ⑩  15  and  30.

   The HCF of 20 and 30 is 10.

(b)    The factors of  14  are    1,  ②  7    and  14.

   The factors of  12  are    1,  ②  3,    4,    6 and  12.

   The HCF of 14 and 12 is  2.

## Example 2

Find the HCF of  60  and  72.

## Solution

Using factor trees:

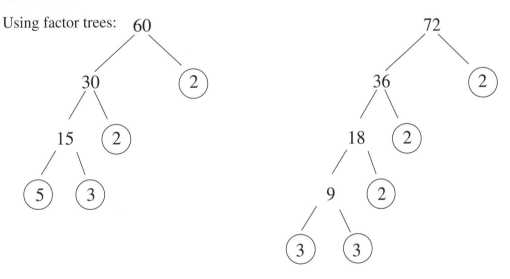

$$60 \ = \ 2 \times 2 \times 3 \times 5$$
$$= \ 2^2 \times 3 \times 5$$

$$72 \ = \ 2 \times 2 \times 2 \times 3 \times 3$$
$$= \ 2^3 \times 3^2$$

The HCF is calculated using the prime factors that are common to both numbers. In this case, 2 appears twice in both, and 3 appears once in both.

So,

   the HCF of 60 and 72  $= \ 2 \times 2 \times 3$

                                            $= \ 12$

To be in the HCF, the prime factor must be in *both* lists:

$$60 = 2 \times 2 \qquad \times 3 \qquad \times 5$$
$$72 = 2 \times 2 \times 2 \times 3 \times 3$$
$$\overline{\text{HCF} = 2 \times 2 \qquad \times 3}$$

$$\text{HCF} = 12$$

Alternatively, using indices:

$$60 = 2^2 \times 3^1 \times 5^1$$
$$72 = 2^3 \times 3^2 \times 5^0$$

*Lowest power of 3*

$$\text{HCF} = 2^2 \times 3^1 \times 5^0$$

*Lowest power of 2*     *Lowest power of 5*

$$\text{HCF} = 12$$

> The *lowest common multiple* (LCM) of two numbers is the smallest number that is a multiple of both.

For example, 18 is the smallest number that is a multiple of both 6 and 9, so the LCM of 6 and 9 is 18.

## Example 3

What is the LCM of:

(a)    5 and 7                    (b)    6 and 10

## Solution

(a)    The multiples of 5 are:

5,  10,  15,  20,  25,  30,  (35,)  40,  45,  ...

The multiples of 7 are:

7,  14,  21,  28,  (35,)  42,  49,  ...

The LCM of 5 and 7 = 35.

(b)    The multiples of 6 are:

6,  12,  18,  24,  (30,)  36,  42,  ...

The multiples of 10 are:

10,  20,  (30,)  40,  50,  60,  ...

The LCM of 6 and 10 = 30.

The LCM for larger numbers can be found by using prime factorisation.

## Example 4

Find the LCM of 60 and 72.

## Solution

From Example 2,

$60 = 2 \times 2 \times 3 \times 5 = 2^2 \times 3 \times 5$ and $72 = 2 \times 2 \times 2 \times 3 \times 3 = 2^3 \times 3^2$

The LCM includes all the factors from either number.

To be in the LCM, the prime factor can be in *either* list or in *both* lists:

$60 = 2 \times 2 \qquad \times 3 \qquad \times 5$
$72 = 2 \times 2 \times 2 \times 3 \times 3$

LCM $= 2 \times 2 \times 2 \times 3 \times 3 \times 5$

LCM $= 360$

Alternatively, using indices:

$60 = 2^2 \times 3^1 \times 5^1$
$72 = 2^3 \times 3^2 \times 5^0$

*Highest power of 3*

LCM $= 2^3 \times 3^2 \times 5^1$

*Highest power of 2*        *Highest power of 5*

LCM $= 360$

## Example 5

Find the HCF and LCM of 50 and 70.

## Solution

Using factor trees to find the prime factorisations:

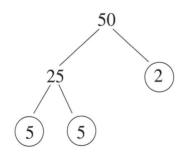

$50 = 2 \times 5 \times 5$
$= 2^1 \times 5^2$

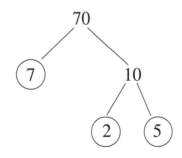

$70 = 2 \times 5 \times 7$
$= 2^1 \times 5^1 \times 7^1$

$$\text{HCF} = 2^1 \times 5^1 \times 7^0$$
$$= 10$$

$$\text{LCM} = 2^1 \times 5^2 \times 7^1$$
$$= 350$$

$$\text{HCF} = 2 \times 5$$

| | | |
|---|---|---|
| $50$ | $= 2 \times 5 \times 5$ | |
| $70$ | $= 2 \times 5$ | $\times 7$ |

$$\text{LCM} = 2 \times 5 \times 5 \times 7$$

## Exercises

1. (a) List the factors of 21.

   (b) List the factors of 35.

   (c) What is the HCF of 21 and 35 ?

2. Find the HCF of:

   (a) 6 and 9                        (b) 14 and 18

   (c) 30 and 24                  (d) 15 and 10

3. (a) Use a factor tree to find the prime factorisation of 42.

   (b) Use a factor tree to find the prime factorisation of 90.

   (c) Find the HCF of 42 and 90.

4. What is the HCF of:

   (a) 90 and 120      (b) 96 and 72      (c) 56 and 60

   (d) 77 and 50       (e) 300 and 550    (f) 320 and 128 ?

5. (a) List the first 10 multiples of 8.

   (b) List the first 10 multiples of 6.

   (c) What is the LCM of 6 and 8 ?

6. What is the LCM of:

   (a) 5 and 3          (b) 9 and 6         (c) 8 and 10

   (d) 12 and 9        (e) 15 and 20     (f) 6 and 11 ?

7. (a) Use a factor tree to find the prime factorisation of 66.

   (b) Use a factor tree to find the prime factorisation of 40.

   (c) Find the LCM of 40 and 66.

8.    Find the LCM of:

(a)    28 and 30         (b)    16 and 24         (c)    20 and 25

(d)    60 and 50         (e)    12 and 18         (f)    21 and 35

9.    Two lighthouses can be seen from the top of a hill. The first flashes once every 8 seconds, and the other flashes once every 15 seconds.  If they flash simultaneously, how long is it until they flash again at the same time?

10.    At a go-kart race track, Vic completes a lap in 40 seconds; Paul completes a lap in 30 seconds, and Mark completes a lap in 50 seconds.

If all three start a lap at the same time, how long is it before

(a)    Paul overtakes Vic,

(b)    Vic overtakes Mark?

# 2.5  Squares and Square Roots

> To *square* a number you multiply the number by itself.

If you square 8, you multiply 8 by 8:

$$8 \times 8 = 64$$

so the square of 8 = 64.

The calculator button for squaring numbers usually looks like $\boxed{x^2}$ or $\boxed{x^2}$.  For the second type of calculator you have to press the  SHIFT  or 2nd FUNCTION key first.

Sometimes we need to answer questions such as,

"What number was squared to get 64?"

When answering this we need to use square roots.

> The *square root* of a number is a number which, when squared (multiplied by itself), gives you the first number.
>
> The sign  $\sqrt{\phantom{x}}$  means *square root*.

We say that:

the square root of  64  is  8,  i.e.   $\sqrt{64} = 8$

since the square of  8  is  64,  i.e.   $8^2 = 64$

The calculator button for finding a square root usually looks like $\boxed{\sqrt{\phantom{x}}}$ .
With some calculators you press the square root button *before* entering the
number; with others you enter the number and *then* press the square root button.
You need to find out how your calculator works out square roots.

## Example 1

(a)  Square each of these numbers:

     1,  5,  7,  14

(b)  Find:

     $\sqrt{25}$,  $\sqrt{49}$,  $\sqrt{196}$,  $\sqrt{1}$

## Solution

(a)   $1^2 \ = \ 1 \times 1 \ = \ 1$

     $5^2 \ = \ 5 \times 5 \ = \ 25$

     $7^2 \ = \ 7 \times 7 \ = \ 49$

     $14^2 \ = \ 14 \times 14 \ = 196$

(b)   $\sqrt{25} \ = \ 5$          because $5^2 = 25$

     $\sqrt{49} \ = \ 7$          because $7^2 = 49$

     $\sqrt{196} \ = \ 14$        because $14^2 = 196$

     $\sqrt{1} \ = \ 1$          because $1^2 = 1$

## Example 2

Use your calculator to find:

(a)  $54^2$

(b)  $\sqrt{961}$

## Solution

(a)  Either $\boxed{5}\ \boxed{4}\ \boxed{x^2}\ \boxed{=}$ 2916   *or*   $\boxed{5}\ \boxed{4}\ \boxed{\text{SHIFT}}\ \boxed{x^2}\ \boxed{=}$ 2916

(b)  Either $\boxed{9}\ \boxed{6}\ \boxed{1}\ \boxed{\sqrt{\phantom{x}}}\ \boxed{=}$ 31   *or*   $\boxed{\sqrt{\phantom{x}}}\ \boxed{9}\ \boxed{6}\ \boxed{1}\ \boxed{=}$ 31

## Example 3

The area of this square is $225 \text{ cm}^2$.
What is the length of each side?

225 cm$^2$

## Solution

$$\text{Area} = (\text{length of side})^2$$

$$225 \text{ cm}^2 = (\text{length of side})^2$$

$$\text{Length of side} = \sqrt{225}$$

$$= 15 \text{ cm}$$

## Example 4

Use your calculator to find $\sqrt{5}$ correct to 2 decimal places.

## Solution

$$\sqrt{5} = 2.236067977$$

$$= 2.24 \text{ correct to 2 decimal places.}$$

## Exercises

1.  (a)  Square these numbers:

$$2, \quad 4, \quad 9, \quad 11, \quad 12, \quad 18, \quad 20$$

(b)  Use your answers to (a) to find:

$$\sqrt{144}, \quad \sqrt{16}, \quad \sqrt{121}, \quad \sqrt{4}, \quad \sqrt{81}, \quad \sqrt{400}, \quad \sqrt{324}$$

2.  Write down the following square roots *without* using a calculator:

(a)  $\sqrt{9}$       (b)  $\sqrt{36}$       (c)  $\sqrt{100}$

(d)  $\sqrt{169}$       (e)  $\sqrt{225}$       (f)  $\sqrt{0}$

3.  Use a calculator to find these square roots, giving your answers correct to 2 decimal places:

(a)  $\sqrt{6}$       (b)  $\sqrt{10}$       (c)  $\sqrt{12}$

(d)  $\sqrt{20}$       (e)  $\sqrt{50}$       (f)  $\sqrt{90}$

4.    What are the lengths of the sides of a square which has an area of 81 cm$^2$ ?

5.    A square has an area of 140 cm$^2$. How long are the sides of this square, to the nearest mm?

6.    Explain why  $7 < \sqrt{51} < 8$.

7.    Copy the statements below and complete each one, putting two *consecutive* whole numbers in the empty spaces:

      (a)  $\boxed{\phantom{x}} < \sqrt{70} < \boxed{\phantom{x}}$          (b)  $\boxed{\phantom{x}} < \sqrt{90} < \boxed{\phantom{x}}$

      (c)  $\boxed{\phantom{x}} < \sqrt{5} < \boxed{\phantom{x}}$          (d)  $\boxed{\phantom{x}} < \sqrt{2} < \boxed{\phantom{x}}$

      (e)  $\boxed{\phantom{x}} < \sqrt{115} < \boxed{\phantom{x}}$          (f)  $\boxed{\phantom{x}} < \sqrt{39} < \boxed{\phantom{x}}$

8.    Decide whether each of these statements is *true* or *false*:

      (a)  $4 < \sqrt{10} < 5$               (b)  $2.6 < \sqrt{7} < 2.7$

      (c)  $3.4 < \sqrt{12} < 3.5$            (d)  $3.7 < \sqrt{15} < 3.8$

      Write correct statements to replace those that are *false*, but keep the same square roots in them.

9.    What is the perimeter of a square with area 196 cm$^2$ ?

10.   Three identical squares are put side-by-side to form a rectangle. The area of the rectangle is 192 cm$^2$. What are the lengths of the sides of the rectangle?

# 3 Pythagoras' Theorem

## 3.1 Pythagoras' Theorem

Pythagoras' Theorem relates the length of the *hypotenuse* of a right-angled triangle to the lengths of the other two sides.

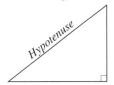

The hypotenuse is always the longest side: it is always the side opposite the right angle.

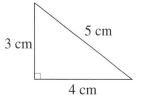

The diagram opposite shows a right-angled triangle. The length of the hypotenuse is 5 cm and the other two sides have lengths 3 cm and 4 cm.

In this diagram, a square, A, has been drawn on the 3 cm side.

$$\text{Area of square A} = 3 \times 3$$
$$= 9 \text{ cm}^2$$

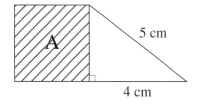

In this diagram, a second square, B, has been drawn on the 4 cm side.

$$\text{Area of square B} = 4 \times 4$$
$$= 16 \text{ cm}^2$$

Squares A and B together have total area:

$$\text{Area A} + \text{Area B} = 9 + 16$$
$$= 25 \text{ cm}^2$$

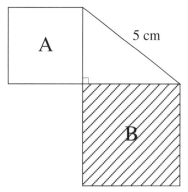

Finally, a third square, C, has been drawn on the 5 cm side.

$$\text{Area of square C} = 5 \times 5$$
$$= 25 \text{ cm}^2$$

We can see that
$$\text{Area A} + \text{Area B} = \text{Area C}.$$

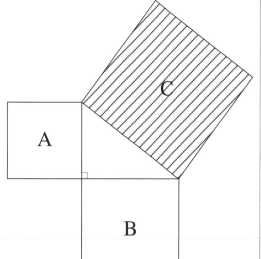

This formula is *always* true for right-angled triangles.

We now look at a right-angled triangle with sides *a*, *b* and *c*, as shown opposite.

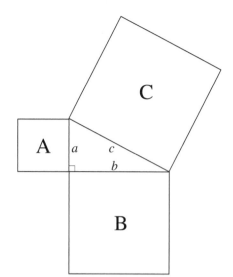

$$\text{Area A} = a \times a$$
$$= a^2$$
$$\text{Area B} = b \times b$$
$$= b^2$$
$$\text{Area C} = c \times c$$
$$= c^2$$

So,

$$\text{Area A} + \text{Area B} = \text{Area C}$$

gives us the formula

$$a^2 + b^2 = c^2$$

for all right-angled triangles.

Pythagoras' Theorem states that, for any right-angled triangle, the area of the square on the hypotenuse is equal to the sum of the areas of the squares on the two shorter sides.

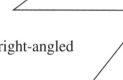

If we use the letters *a*, *b* and *c* for the sides of a right-angled triangle, then Pythagoras' Theorem states that

$$a^2 + b^2 = c^2$$

where *c* is the length of the hypotenuse.

## Example 1

Verify Pythagoras' Theorem for the right-angled triangle opposite:

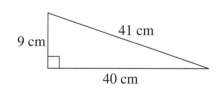

## Solution

Here $a = 9$ cm, $b = 40$ cm, $c = 41$ cm.

$$a^2 = 9^2 = 9 \times 9 = 81$$
$$b^2 = 40^2 = 40 \times 40 = 1600$$

$$a^2 + b^2 = 1681$$

$$c^2 = 41^2 = 41 \times 41 = 1681$$

So $a^2 + b^2 = c^2$ for this triangle.

## Exercises

1. Which side is the *hypotenuse* in each of the following right angled triangles:

(a)
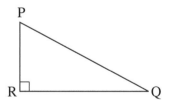

(b)
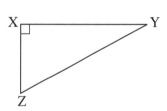

(c)
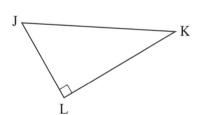

(d)
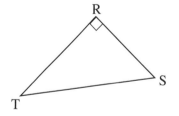

2. For each of the three diagrams at the top of the next page:

   (i) calculate the area of square A,

   (ii) calculate the area of square B,

   (iii) calculate the sum of area A and area B,

   (iv) calculate the area of square C,

   (v) check that :

   $$\text{area A} + \text{area B} = \text{area C}$$

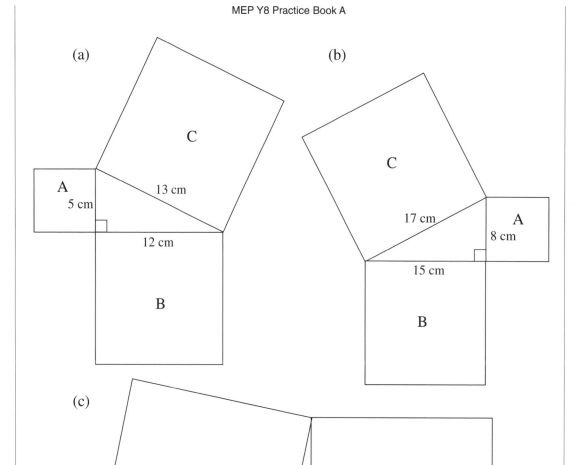

3. Using the method shown in Example 1, verify Pythagoras' Theorem for the right-angled triangles below:

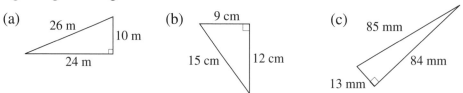

4. The whole numbers 3, 4, 5 are called a *Pythagorean triple* because
$3^2 + 4^2 = 5^2$. A triangle with sides of lengths 3 cm, 4 cm and 5 cm is right-angled.

Use Pythagoras' Theorem to determine which of the sets of numbers below are Pythagorean triples:

(a)    15, 20, 25            (b)    10, 24, 26

(c)    11, 22, 30            (d)    6, 8, 9

# 3.2 Calculating the Length of the Hypotenuse

Pythagoras' Theorem states that, for a right-angled triangle,

$$c^2 = a^2 + b^2$$

With this result it is very easy to calculate the
length of the hypotenuse of a right-angled triangle.

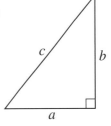

## Example 1

Calculate the length of the hypotenuse of a
triangle in which the other two sides are of
lengths 7 m and 8 m.

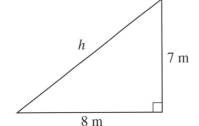

### Solution

Let $h$ be the length of the hypotenuse.

By Pythagoras' Theorem,

$$h^2 = 8^2 + 7^2$$

$$h^2 = 64 + 49$$

$$h^2 = 113$$

$$h = \sqrt{113}$$

$$h = 10.63014581 \text{ m}$$

$$h = 10.6 \text{ m, correct to 1 decimal place}$$

## Example 2

Calculate the length of the diagonals of the
rectangle opposite:

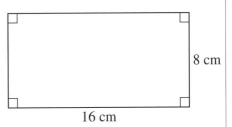

16 cm

8 cm

### Solution

The diagram shows the right-angled triangle
that you need to use to find the length of the
diagonal. The hypotenuse is the diagonal of
the rectangle and this is labelled $d$ on the
diagram.

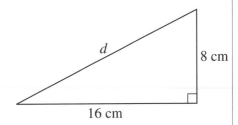

By Pythagoras' Theorem,

$$d^2 = 16^2 + 8^2$$

$$= 256 + 64$$

$$= 320$$

$$d = \sqrt{320}$$

$$d = 17.88854382 \text{ cm}$$

$$d = 17.9 \text{ cm, correct to 1 decimal place}$$

## Exercises

1.  Calculate the length of the hypotenuse of each of these triangles:

    (a)
    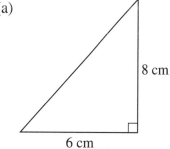

    (b)
    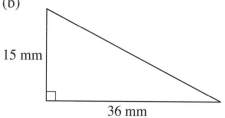

    (c)
    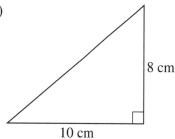

    (d)
    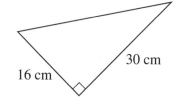

2.  Calculate the length of the hypotenuse of each of the following triangles, giving your answers correct to 1 decimal place.

    (a)

    (b)

    (c)

    (d)
    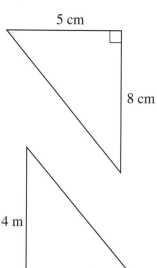

3. A rectangle has sides of lengths 5 cm and 10 cm.

   How long is the diagonal of the rectangle?

4. Calculate the length of the diagonal of a square with sides of length 6 cm.

5. The diagram shows a wooden frame
   that is to be part of the roof of a house:

   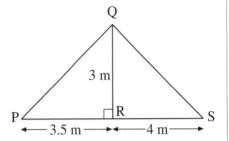

   (a) Use Pythagoras' Theorem in triangle
       PQR to find the length PQ.

   (b) Calculate the length QS.

   (c) Calculate the total length of wood
       needed to make the frame.

6. An isosceles triangle has a base of length 4 cm
   and perpendicular height 8 cm. Giving your
   answers correct to 1 decimal place, calculate:

   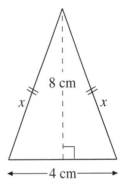

   (a) the length, $x$ cm, of one of the equal sides,

   (b) the perimeter of the triangle.

7. One end of a rope is tied to the top of a
   vertical flagpole of height 5.2 m. When the
   rope is pulled tight, the other end is on the
   ground 3.8 m from the base of the flagpole.

   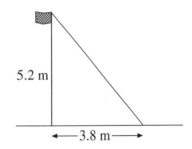

   Calculate the length of the rope, giving
   your answer correct to 1 decimal place.

8. A rectangular lawn is 12.5 m long and 8 m wide. Matthew walks diagonally
   across the lawn from one corner to the other. He returns to the first corner
   by walking round the edge of the lawn. How much further does he walk on
   his return journey?

9. Which of the rectangles below has the longer diagonal?

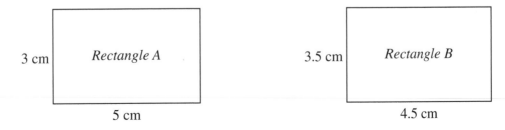

10.

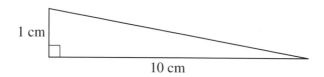

(a)    Use Pythagoras' Theorem to show that the length of the hypotenuse
       of this triangle is 10.0 cm correct to 1 decimal place.

(b)    Maxine says that this triangle is isosceles because there are two
       sides of the same length.

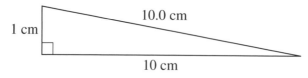

Is Maxine correct?

# 3.3 Calculating the Lengths of Other Sides

## Example 1

Calculate the length of the side marked $x$ in the following triangle:

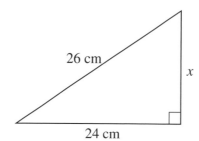

### Solution

By Pythagoras' Theorem:

$$x^2 + 24^2 = 26^2$$

$$x^2 + 576 = 676$$

$$x^2 = 676 - 576$$

$$x^2 = 100$$

$$x = \sqrt{100}$$

$$x = 10$$

The length of the side $x$ is 10 cm.

## Example 2

Calculate the perpendicular height of the isosceles triangle shown opposite:

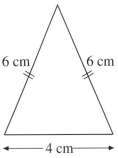

6 cm    6 cm

4 cm

## Solution

The height can be calculated by using half of the original isosceles triangle, as shown:

The height has been labelled $h$ on the diagram.

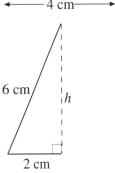

6 cm    $h$

2 cm

By Pythagoras' Theorem:

$$h^2 + 2^2 = 6^2$$
$$h^2 + 4 = 36$$
$$h^2 = 36 - 4$$
$$h^2 = 32$$
$$h = \sqrt{32}$$
$$h = 5.656854249$$

The perpendicular height of the triangle is 5.7 cm to 1 decimal place.

## Exercises

1.  Calculate the length of the side marked $x$ in each of the following triangles:

(a)

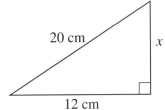

20 cm    $x$

12 cm

(b)

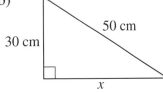

50 cm

30 cm

$x$

(c)

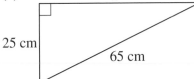

$x$

25 cm

65 cm

(d)

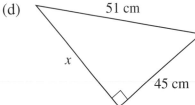

51 cm

$x$

45 cm

2.  Calculate the length of the side marked $x$ in each of the following triangles, giving your answer correct to 1 decimal place:

(a)

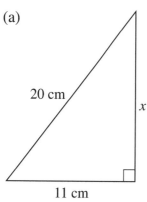

20 cm

$x$

11 cm

(b)

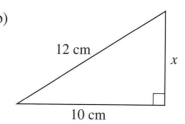

12 cm

$x$

10 cm

(c)

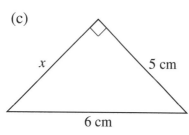

$x$

5 cm

6 cm

(d)

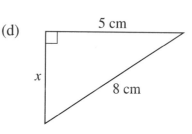

5 cm

$x$

8 cm

3.  Calculate the perpendicular height of this equilateral triangle, giving your answer correct to 1 decimal place.

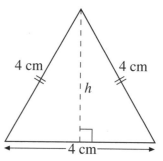

4 cm        4 cm

$h$

4 cm

4.  Calculate the perpendicular height of an equilateral triangle with sides of length 5 cm, giving your answer correct to 1 decimal place.

5.  Calculate the perpendicular height of the isosceles triangle shown opposite, giving your answer correct to 1 decimal place.

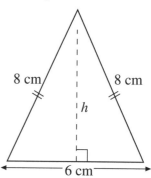

8 cm        8 cm

$h$

6 cm

6.  The width of a rectangle is 5 cm and the length of its diagonal is 13 cm.

    (a)   How long is the other side of the rectangle?

    (b)   What is the area of the rectangle?

7.  The isosceles triangle at the top of the next page has 2 sides of length $x$ cm. Copy and complete the calculation to find the value of $x$ correct to 1 decimal place.

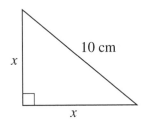

By Pythagoras' Theorem,

$$x^2 + x^2 = 10^2$$

$$2x^2 = 100$$

$$x^2 = $$

$$x = \sqrt{\phantom{x}}$$

$$x = $$

$$x = \qquad \text{to 1 decimal place.}$$

8.    The length of the diagonal of a square is 8 cm. How long are the sides of the square?

9.    The diagram shows part of the framework of a roof.

   (a)    Calculate the length XZ.

   (b)    Calculate the length of YZ, correct to 1 decimal place.

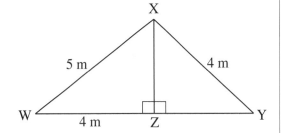

10.   A sheet is stretched over a washing line to make a tent, as shown in the diagram.

   (a)    How high is the washing line above the ground? Give your answer to 1 decimal place.

   (b)    If the same sheet was used and the washing line was now at a height of 1.25 m above the ground, what would be the width of the base of the tent? Give your answer correct to 1 decimal place.

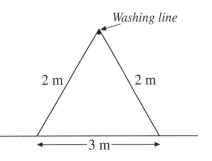

11.   A fishing rod is used to catch plastic ducks in a fairground game. The rod is 1 m long. A string with a ring is tied to the end of the rod. The length of the string is 0.4 m.

   When the ring is level with the lower end of the rod, as shown in the diagram, how far is the ring from that end of the fishing rod?

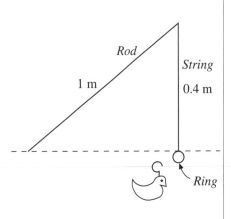

# 3.4 Problems in Context

When we use Pythagoras' Theorem to solve problems in context the first key step is to draw a right-angled triangle.

## Example 1

A ladder is 5 m long. The bottom of the ladder is 2 m from the foot of a wall and the top leans against the wall. How high is the top of the ladder above the ground?

## Solution

The first step is to draw a triangle to represent the situation. The height to the top of the ladder has been labelled $h$. (We assume that the ground is horizontal and the wall is vertical.)

Now use Pythagoras' Theorem:

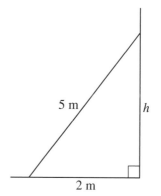

$$h^2 + 2^2 = 5^2$$

$$h^2 + 4 = 25$$

$$h^2 = 25 - 4 = 21$$

$$h = \sqrt{21}$$

$$h = 4.582575695$$

The top of the ladder is 4.58 m above the ground (to the nearest cm).

## Example 2

A ship sails 300 km due west and then 100 km due south. At the end of this journey, how far is the ship from its starting position?

## Solution

The first step is to draw a diagram showing the ship's journey. The distance from the starting point has been labelled $d$.

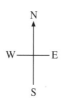
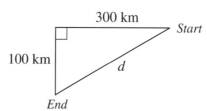

Now use Pythagoras Theorem:

$$d^2 = 300^2 + 100^2$$

$$d^2 = 90\,000 + 10\,000$$

$$d^2 = 100\,000$$

$$d = \sqrt{100\,000}$$

$$d = 316.227766$$

The distance from the starting point is 316 km to the nearest km.

## Example 3

Calculate the area of the triangle shown opposite:

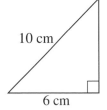

## Solution

The length of the unknown side has been marked $x$.

Using Pythagoras' Theorem,

$$x^2 + 6^2 = 10^2$$

$$x^2 + 36 = 100$$

$$x^2 = 100 - 36$$

$$x^2 = 64$$

$$x = \sqrt{64}$$

$$x = 8 \text{ cm}$$

$$\text{Area of the triangle} = \frac{1}{2} \times \text{base} \times \text{perpendicular height}$$

$$= \frac{1}{2} \times 6 \times 8$$

$$= 24 \text{ cm}^2$$

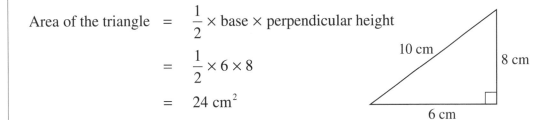

## Exercises

1. A hiker walks 300 m due north and then 400 m due east. How far is the hiker now from her starting position?

2. A ladder of length 4 m leans against a wall so that the top of the ladder is 3 m above ground level. How far is the bottom of the ladder from the wall?

3. Two remote-controlled cars set off from the same position. After a short time one has travelled 20 m due north and the other 15 m due east. How far apart are the two cars?

4. A room should have a rectangular floor, with sides of lengths 4 m and 5 m. A builder wants to check that the room is a perfect rectangle and measures the two diagonals of the room, which should be the same length. To the nearest cm, how long should each diagonal be?

5. For the triangle shown opposite,

   (a) calculate the length $x$,

   (b) calculate the area of the triangle.

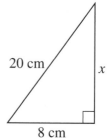

20 cm   $x$

8 cm

6. Calculate the perimeter of the triangle shown opposite, giving your answer correct to 1 decimal place.

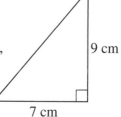

9 cm

7 cm

7. Calculate the perimeter of the parallelogram below, giving your answer to the nearest millimetre.

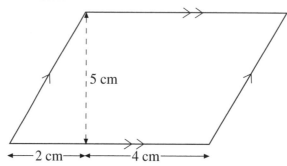

5 cm

2 cm   4 cm

8. One end of a rope of length 10 m is tied to the top of a vertical flag pole. When the rope is tight it can touch the ground at a distance of 4 m from the base of the pole. How tall is the flagpole? Give your answer correct to the nearest cm.

9. A guy rope on a tent is 1.5 m long. One end is fixed to the top of a vertical pole and the other is pegged to the ground. If the pole is 1.2 m high, how far is the pegged end of the rope from the base of the flagpole?

10. Ron's dad says that Ron must not walk on the lawn. The lawn is a rectangle with sides of lengths 10 m and 16 m. When his dad is looking, Ron walks from his house to the gate by walking along two edges of the lawn. When his dad is not looking, Ron walks diagonally across the lawn.

    How much further does Ron have to walk to get from the house to the gate when his dad is looking? Give your answer to a suitable level of accuracy.

# 3.5 Constructions and Angles

The formula for Pythagoras' Theorem can be used to decide if a triangle is right-angled.

In any triangle,

> the *longest side* faces the *largest angle*
>
> the *shortest side* faces the *smallest angle*.

In a triangle with longest side $c$, and other two sides $a$ and $b$,

> if $c^2 = a^2 + b^2$, then the angle opposite $c = 90°$;
>
> if $c^2 < a^2 + b^2$, then the angle opposite $c < 90°$
> (so all three angles are acute);
>
> if $c^2 > a^2 + b^2$, then the angle opposite $c > 90°$
> (i.e. the triangle has an obtuse angle).

## Example 1

(a)  Use a ruler and a pair of compasses to construct this triangle:

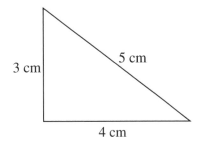

3 cm

5 cm

4 cm

(b)  Use a protractor to check that the triangle has a right angle.

(c)  Confirm that Pythagoras' Theorem is true for this triangle.

## Solution

(a)  First draw a line with length 4 cm.

Then draw an arc of radius 3 cm with centre on the left-hand end of the line.

Next draw an arc of radius 5 cm with centre on the right-hand end of the line.

The point where the two arcs cross is the third corner of the triangle.

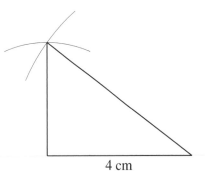

4 cm

(b)  The angle at the bottom left-hand corner
measures $90°$, so the triangle has a
right angle.

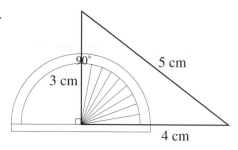

(c)  Here  $a = 4$ cm,  $b = 3$ cm  and  $c = 5$ cm.

$$a^2 + b^2 = 4^2 + 3^2$$
$$= 16 + 9$$
$$= 25$$

$$c^2 = 5^2$$
$$= 25$$

Therefore

$$a^2 + b^2 = c^2$$

So Pythagoras' Theorem is true in this case, confirming that this is a right-
angled triangle.

## Example 2

Which of these triangles contains a right angle?

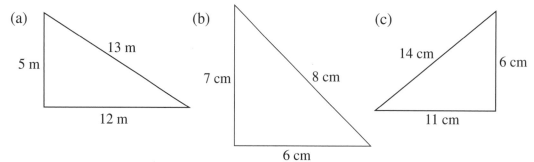

## Solution

We use Pythagoras' Theorem to find out if a triangle is right-angled, using $c$ for
the longest side.

(a)  In this triangle,  $a = 5$,  $b = 12$ and $c = 13$.

$$a^2 + b^2 = 5^2 + 12^2 \qquad\qquad c^2 = 13^2$$
$$= 25 + 144 \qquad\qquad\qquad = 169$$
$$= 169$$

Here  $a^2 + b^2 = c^2$,  so this triangle does contain a right angle.

(b)    In this triangle, $a = 6$, $b = 7$ and $c = 8$.

$$a^2 + b^2 = 6^2 + 7^2 \qquad\qquad c^2 = 8^2$$
$$= 36 + 49 \qquad\qquad\qquad\quad = 64$$
$$= 85$$

Here $c^2 \neq a^2 + b^2$, so the triangle does not contain a right angle.  As $c^2 < a^2 + b^2$, the angle opposite $c$ is less than $90\,°$, so all the angles in this triangle are acute.

(c)    Here $a = 6$, $b = 11$ and $c = 14$.

$$a^2 + b^2 = 6^2 + 11^2 \qquad\qquad c^2 = 14^2$$
$$= 36 + 121 \qquad\qquad\qquad\quad = 196$$
$$= 157$$

Here $c^2 \neq a^2 + b^2$, so the triangle does not contain a right angle.  As $c^2 > a^2 + b^2$ the angle opposite $c$ is greater than $90\,°$, so the triangle contains one obtuse angle.

## Exercises

1.    (a)    Using a ruler and a pair of compasses, construct a triangle with sides of lengths  6 cm, 8 cm and 10 cm.

      (b)    Use a protractor to measure the angles of your triangle.

      (c)    Is the triangle right-angled?

      (d)    Use Pythagoras' Theorem to decide whether the triangle is right-angled.

      (e)    Was your answer to part (c) correct?

2.    Repeat question 2 for a triangle with sides of lengths  7 cm, 8 cm and 11 cm.

3.    Decide which of the triangles described below:

      (a)    is right-angled,

      (b)    contains an obtuse angle,

      (c)    contains all acute angles.

      In each case, show how you reached your conclusion.

              (i)    *a triangle with sides of lengths  10 cm, 11 cm and 14 cm*

              (ii)   *a triangle with sides of lengths  10 cm, 12 cm and 16 cm*

              (iii)  *a triangle with sides of lengths  9 cm, 12 cm and 15 cm*

4.   (a)   Use an accurate construction to find out if a triangle with sides of lengths 6 cm, 7 cm and 12 cm contains a right angle.

     (b)   Use Pythagoras' Theorem to check your answer to part (a).

5.   Ahmed draws a square with sides of length 6 cm. He then measures a diagonal as 8.2 cm.
     Use Pythagoras' Theorem to decide if Ahmed has drawn the square accurately.

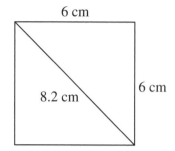

6.   An isosceles triangle has 2 sides of length 8 cm. The length of the base is 9 cm.

     Decide, by calculation, whether the angle $\theta$ is a right angle, an acute angle or an obtuse angle. Show clearly how you reached your conclusion.

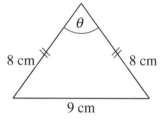

7.   Measure the lengths of the sides and diagonal of your textbook. Use your measurements to decide whether the corners of your book are right-angled.

8.   A triangle has sides of lengths 21 cm, 28 cm and $x$ cm.

     (a)   Show that the triangle has a right angle if $x = 35$.

     (b)   For what values of $x$ will the triangle contain an *obtuse* angle?

9.   An isosceles triangle is known to have one side of length 18 cm and one side of length 28 cm.

     (a)   Explain why the triangle cannot contain a right angle,

     (b)   Show, by calculation, that it is possible for the triangle to contain three acute angles. Draw a sketch of the triangle in this case.

10.  A right-angled triangle has two sides of lengths 24 cm and 32 cm. Use Pythagoras' Theorem to calculate the length of the other side.
     [Note: there are 2 possible answers.]

# 4 Rounding and Estimating

## 4.1 Revision of the Four Rules: Whole Numbers

### Example 1

Calculate:

(a)　464 + 97

(b)　184 − 36

(c)　47 × 12

(d)　710 ÷ 5

### Solution

(a)
```
    4 6 4
  +   9 7
  -------
    5 6 1
    1 1
```

(b)
```
    7 1
  1 8̸ 4
  -   3 6
  -------
    1 4 8
```

(c)
```
      4 7
  ×   1 2
  -------
      9 4
    4 7 0
  -------
    5 6 4
    1
```

(d)
```
      1 4 2
      2 1
  5 | 7 1 0
```

### Exercises

Work out the answer to each question *without* using a calculator.  Check your answers with a calculator.

1.　(a)　13 + 16　　(b)　24 + 22　　(c)　45 + 34

　　(d)　123 + 51　　(e)　214 + 135　　(f)　201 + 356

2.　(a)　36 + 102　　(b)　88 + 35　　(c)　66 + 282

　　(d)　97 + 142　　(e)　361 + 421　　(f)　188 + 924

3.　(a)　25 − 13　　(b)　66 − 22　　(c)　97 − 46

　　(d)　136 − 121　　(e)　258 − 39　　(f)　971 − 420

4.    (a)    $199 - 42$          (b)    $643 - 132$          (c)    $198 - 156$

      (d)    $372 - 184$         (e)    $924 - 138$          (f)    $3631 - 179$


5.    (a)    $12 \times 3$       (b)    $11 \times 5$        (c)    $23 \times 2$

      (d)    $31 \times 3$       (e)    $22 \times 4$        (f)    $101 \times 6$


6.    (a)    $19 \times 5$       (b)    $86 \times 4$        (c)    $39 \times 6$

      (d)    $27 \times 7$       (e)    $43 \times 9$        (f)    $65 \times 8$


7.    (a)    $82 \times 11$      (b)    $37 \times 12$       (c)    $39 \times 42$

      (d)    $54 \times 23$      (e)    $61 \times 34$       (f)    $87 \times 65$


8.    (a)    $68 \div 2$         (b)    $64 \div 4$          (c)    $123 \div 3$

      (d)    $845 \div 5$        (e)    $312 \div 6$         (f)    $1407 \div 7$


9.    (a)    $240 \div 20$       (b)    $720 \div 12$        (c)    $880 \div 44$

      (d)    $630 \div 15$       (e)    $750 \div 25$        (f)    $345 \div 23$


10.   (a)    $87 \times 3$       (b)    $192 + 249$          (c)    $186 - 95$

      (d)    $36 \times 43$      (e)    $915 \div 5$         (f)    $48 \times 17$


# 4.2  Revision of the Four Rules: Decimals

## Example 1

Calculate:

(a)    $3.8 + 10.42$                          (b)    $18.2 - 0.36$

(c)    $8.2 \times 3.7$                       (d)    $1.56 \div 0.3$

## Solution

(a)        3 . 8                              (b)        $1\overset{7}{8}.\overset{1}{2}\overset{1}{0}$
       $+ \, 1\,0 . 4\,2$                            $- \quad 0 . 3\,6$
       $\overline{\phantom{+}1\,4 . 2\,2}$          $\overline{\phantom{-}1\,7 . 8\,4}$
               1

(c)
$$
\begin{array}{r}
8 \,.\, 2 \\
\times \quad 3 \,.\, 7 \\
\hline
5 \; 7 \; 4 \\
2 \; 4 \; 6 \; 0 \\
\hline
3 \; 0 \,.\, 3 \; 4 \\
\hline
{\scriptstyle 1} \\
\end{array}
$$

(d) $1.56 \div 0.3 = 15.6 \div 3$

$$
\begin{array}{r}
5 \,.\, 2 \\
\hline
3\,|\,1\;5\,.\,6 \\
\end{array}
$$

## Exercises

Solve each of the following *without* using a calculator.  Check your answers with a calculator.

1.  (a)  $3.5 + 4.2$      (b)  $16.1 + 32.6$      (c)  $1.5 + 3.8$

    (d)  $13.3 + 4.61$      (e)  $18.6 + 0.42$      (f)  $3.14 + 0.612$

2.  (a)  $6.4 - 2.1$      (b)  $27.8 - 13.6$      (c)  $3.2 - 0.8$

    (d)  $8.2 - 4.5$      (e)  $6.62 - 0.34$      (f)  $8.3 - 6.27$

3.  (a)  $4.3 \times 2$      (b)  $3.5 \times 4$      (c)  $7.4 \times 6$

    (d)  $6.2 \times 7$      (e)  $18.3 \times 9$      (f)  $5.62 \times 5$

4.  (a)  $6.8 \div 2$      (b)  $63.9 \div 3$      (c)  $52.4 \div 4$

    (d)  $75.5 \div 5$      (e)  $99.4 \div 7$      (f)  $151.8 \div 6$

5.  (a)  $12.6 + 8.5$      (b)  $76.3 - 18.7$      (c)  $20.39 - 15.6$

    (d)  $17.6 \times 4$      (e)  $132.7 \times 6$      (f)  $36.61 \div 7$

6.  (a)  $5.6 \times 0.3$      (b)  $2.3 \times 1.5$      (c)  $4.8 \times 0.21$

    (d)  $3.4 \times 9.4$      (e)  $3.6 \times 0.72$      (f)  $8.2 \times 0.91$

7.  (a)  $18.6 \div 0.3$      (b)  $74.5 \div 0.5$      (c)  $0.36 \div 0.02$

    (d)  $10.5 \div 5$      (e)  $45 \div 0.09$      (f)  $0.84 \div 0.4$

8.  (a)  $21.6 \div 0.4$      (b)  $8.2 - 0.37$      (c)  $0.62 \times 7$

    (d)  $3.2 \times 0.17$      (e)  $8.4 \div 8$      (f)  $3.7 \times 2.01$

# 4.3  Order of Operations

**B**rackets

**O**

**D**ivision

**M**ultiplication

**A**ddition

**S**ubtraction

**BODMAS** can be used to remember the order in which to carry out operations

### Example 1

Calculate:

(a)  $(3 + 2) \times 6 - 8$

(b)  $4 \times 6 + 18 \div 2$

(c)  $(17 - 2) \div 5 + 6$

### Solution

(a)  $(3 + 2) \times 6 - 8$      *(brackets first)*

$= 5 \times 6 - 8$      *(multiplication second)*

$= 30 - 8$      *(subtraction last)*

$= 22$

(b)  $4 \times 6 + 18 \div 2$      *(multiplication and division must be done before addition)*

$= 24 + 9$

$= 33$

(c)  $(17 - 2) \div 5 + 6$      *(brackets first)*

$= 15 \div 5 + 6$      *(division second)*

$= 3 + 6$      *(addition last)*

$= 9$

### Example 2

State whether each one of the statements below is *true* or *false*:

(a)  $3 + 6 \times 2 = 15$

(b)  $30 - 7 \times 4 = 92$

(c)  $8 + 20 \div 2 = 14$

## Solution

(a)  $3 + 6 \times 2 = 3 + 12$      *(multiplication must be done before addition)*

$\qquad\qquad\quad\; = 15$

Therefore the statement is *true*.

(b)  $30 - 7 \times 4 = 30 - 28$      *(multiplication must be done before subtraction)*

$\qquad\qquad\qquad = 2$

Therefore the statement is *false*.

(c)  $8 + 20 \div 2 = 8 + 10$      *(division must be done before addition)*

$\qquad\qquad\qquad = 18$

Therefore the statement is *false*.

## Exercises

1. Calculate:

   (a)  $6 + 7 \times 2$                (b)  $8 - 3 \times 2$

   (c)  $19 - 4 \times 3$            (d)  $3 \times 6 - 9$

   (e)  $15 - 4 + 7 \times 2$        (f)  $11 \times 3 + 2$

   (g)  $16 \times 4 - 3$            (h)  $6 + 7 \times 2 - 20 \div 4$

   (i)  $18 \times 2 - (4 + 7)$      (j)  $16 - 5 \times 2 + 3$

2. State whether each one of the statements below is *true* or *false*. Calculate the correct answer for those that are *false*.

   (a)  $6 \times 7 - 2 = 40$        (b)  $8 \times (6 - 2) + 3 = 56$

   (c)  $35 - 7 \times 2 = 56$       (d)  $3 + 7 \times 3 = 30$

   (e)  $18 - (4 + 7) = 21$     (f)  $43 - 3 + 2 = 42$

   (g)  $80 \div 2 + 6 = 10$       (h)  $64 - 10 + 2 = 52$

3. Put brackets into each of the statements below to make it correct:

   (a)  $3 \times 6 + 1 = 21$        (b)  $5 + 6 \times 2 = 22$

   (c)  $45 \div 6 + 3 = 5$         (d)  $49 - 3 + 2 = 44$

   (e)  $7 \times 3 + 2 = 35$        (f)  $13 - 4 \times 2 = 18$

4. Write out each of the calculations below, filling in the missing numbers:

(a) $3 \times ? + 2 = 17$            (b) $? \times 5 - 8 = 22$

(c) $(4 + ?) \times 2 = 20$         (d) $6 - ? \times 2 = 0$

(e) $(7 - ?) \times 4 = 20$         (f) $? \div 3 + 4 = 8$

5. Jane writes down:
$$4 \times 7 + 2 \times 3 = 90$$

(a) Explain why her answer is incorrect, and calculate the correct answer.

(b) By using brackets Jane can make her calculation correct. Show how this can be done.

6. Esther and Andy are given this problem:
$$30 \div 6 - 3 + 1$$
Esther says the answer is 1.

Andy says the answer is 11.

(a) Is either of them correct?

(b) Show how Esther could insert brackets to give her answer.

(c) Show how Andy could insert brackets to give his answer.

7. State whether each one of the statements below is *true* or *false*:

(a) $(3 \times 6) \times 2 = 3 \times (6 \times 2)$       (b) $(4 + 2) + 7 = 4 + (2 + 7)$

(c) $(8 - 2) - 1 = 8 - (2 - 1)$         (d) $(8 \div 2) \div 2 = 8 \div (2 \div 2)$

8. Put brackets into each of the calculations below to make it correct:

(a) $13 - 4 - 1 = 10$

(b) $30 - 9 + 2 = 19$

(c) $60 \div 6 \div 3 = 30$

9. Calculate:

(a) $8.2 \div 0.2 - 0.1$            (b) $3.6 \times 0.2 - 0.1$

(c) $8.2 \times (6 - 5.4)$            (d) $2.2 - 0.7 \times 0.2$

10. Write out each of the calculations below, filling in the missing numbers:

(a) $0.8 + ? \times 0.6 = 3.2$        (b) $? \times 0.5 + 6 \times 0.4 = 3.9$

(c) $0.9 + 4.8 \div ? = 6.9$         (d) $2.7 \div ? - 1.4 = 1.6$

# 4.4 Problems in Context

## Example 1

Packets of football stickers cost 32p each. Calculate the total cost of 25 packets of stickers.

### Solution

Working in pence, total cost is

$$
\begin{array}{r}
3\,2 \\
\times \quad 2\,5 \\
\hline
1\,6\,0 \\
6\,4\,0 \\
\hline
8\,0\,0\,\text{p}
\end{array}
$$

Hence the total cost is £8.00.

## Example 2

Tickets for a concert cost £8 each. Rebecca has £50 to spend on tickets for the concert. How many of her friends can she buy tickets for and how much money does she have left from her £50?

### Solution

$$
\begin{array}{r}
6 \quad \text{Remainder } 2 \\
8\,\overline{\big)\,5\,0}
\end{array}
$$

So Rebecca can buy 6 tickets, one for herself and one each for 5 friends. She will have £2 left.

## Example 3

A taxi driver charges his passengers £1.25 plus 64p per mile. Calculate the cost of:

(a)  a 10 mile journey,                    (b)  a 3 mile journey.

### Solution

Working in pounds, total cost is:

(a)  $1.25 + 10 \times 0.64 \; = \; 1.25 + 6.40$

$\qquad\qquad\qquad\qquad = £7.65$

(b)  $1.25 + 3 \times 0.64 \; = \; 1.25 + 1.92$

$\qquad\qquad\qquad\qquad = £3.17$

## Exercises

*In these questions, do* not *use a calculator, and remember to show* all *of your working.*

1. Tickets for a school party cost £1.25 each. Calculate the cost of:

   (a)   3 tickets,                              (b)   14 tickets.

2. CDs cost £9 each in a music shop sale. How many CDs can you buy if you have £48 to spend? How much money will you have left over?

3. A school buys 30 calculators costing £6.99 each. What is the total cost of these calculators? How could you do this calculation in your head?

4. A school mathematics department has £300 to spend on new textbooks. The textbooks cost £7 each. How many books can be bought?

5. Prakesh is paid travelling expenses every time he drives his car for work. He is paid £12 for each journey, plus 14p per mile travelled. How much is he paid for:

   (a)   a 50 mile journey,                    (b)   an 82 mile journey?

6. How many minibuses, each seating 17 pupils are needed to transport 110 pupils?

7. Joanne buys 3 magazines that cost £1.50, £2.45 and 80p. She pays for them with a £10 note. How much change should she get?

8. Ben orders 25 floppy discs for his computer. The discs cost 40p each and he has to pay £3.25 postage. How much does he have to pay in total?

9. A farmer packs his free-range eggs into boxes that each contain half a dozen eggs. One day he collects 119 eggs. How many boxes can he fill and how many eggs does he have left over?

10. Alison buys 6 tapes that cost £8.99 each. She pays for them with three £20 notes. How much change should she get?

# 4.5   Rounding

We *round* numbers when all we need is a *reasonable approximation* rather than the exact value.

The number  8.4236  can be rounded to a specified number of *decimal places*:

$$8.4236 \quad \rightarrow \quad 8.424 \quad \text{to} \quad 3 \text{ decimal places}$$

$$8.4236 \quad \rightarrow \quad 8.42 \quad \text{to} \quad 2 \text{ decimal places}$$

$$8.4236 \quad \rightarrow \quad 8.4 \quad \text{to} \quad 1 \text{ decimal place}$$

The number 173.265 can be rounded to a specified number of *significant figures*:

$$173.265 \rightarrow 173.27 \text{ to } 5 \text{ significant figures}$$

$$173.265 \rightarrow 173 \text{ to } 3 \text{ significant figures}$$

$$173.265 \rightarrow 200 \text{ to } 1 \text{ significant figure}$$

A particular digit in a number will *round up* if the digit that follows it is 5, 6, 7, 8 or 9.

For example, 52.368 = 52.37 (to 2 decimal places).

The digit will *remain unchanged* if the following digit is 0, 1, 2, 3 or 4.

For example, 6.743 = 6.74 (to 3 significant figures).

## Example 1

Round 3647.5 to the nearest:

(a) whole number,

(b) ten (10),

(c) hundred (100),

(d) thousand (1000).

## Solution

(a) 3648    Note that the 7 rounds up to 8, because it is followed by a 5.

(b) 3650    Note that the 4 rounds up to a 5, because it is followed by a 7.

(c) 3600    Note that the 6 is unchanged, because the digit following it in the number is less than 5.

(d) 4000    Note that the 3 rounds up to a 4, because it is followed by a 6.

## Example 2

Write 13.68952 correct to:

(a) 1 decimal place,    (b) 3 decimal places,    (c) 2 decimal places.

## Solution

(a) 13.7    to 1 decimal place.

(b) 13.690    to 3 decimal places.

(c) 13.69    to 2 decimal places.

## Example 3

Write:

(a)    3.642      correct to  2 significant figures,

(b)    314 269   correct to  3 significant figures,

(c)    0.00723   correct to  1 significant figure.

## Solution

(a)    3.6   correct to 2 significant figures.

(b)    314 000   correct to 3 significant figures.  *(Note the need for zeros to replace the remaining digits of the original number, to give a rounded number of comparable size.)*

(c)    0.007   to 1 significant figure.  *(Note that the zeros before the 7 are not significant, so they are not counted.  The 7 is the first significant figure, i.e. it is the first digit that really determines the size of the number.)*

## Exercises

1.    Round each of the numbers below to the nearest whole number:

   (a)    4.3              (b)    2.04             (c)    16.9

   (d)    3.5              (e)    33.49            (f)    18.65


2.    Round each of these numbers to the nearest ten:

   (a)    187              (b)    309              (c)    8

   (d)    35               (e)    44.9             (f)    16.4


3.    The attendance at a football match was 36 475 people.
      Round this number to:

   (a)    the nearest 1000     (b)    the nearest 100     (c)    the nearest 10.


4.    Write each of these numbers correct to 2 decimal places:

   (a)    4.263            (b)    0.0472           (c)    10.8374

   (d)    82.062           (e)    3.445            (f)    9.395


5.    Write each of these numbers correct to 2 significant figures:

   (a)    1.473            (b)    6.254            (c)    3.216

   (d)    10.68            (e)    142              (f)    1374

6.   Write the number  8.645712  correct to:

   (a)   3 decimal places     (b)   4 decimal places     (c)   1 decimal place.

7.   Write the number  147.52  correct to:

   (a)   4 significant figures,          (b)   3 significant figures,

   (c)   2 significant figures,          (d)   1 significant figure.

8.   Write the number  104.735  correct to:

   (a)   the nearest whole number,     (b)   2 decimal places,

   (c)   2 significant figures,          (d)   1 decimal place,

   (e)   1 significant figure.

9.   Write each of the numbers below correct to 3 significant figures:

   (a)   18.47          (b)   0.003265          (c)   147 300

   (d)   62.999          (e)   0.036247          (f)   0.00036945

10.   A student completes the table opposite, but puts the accuracy statements against the wrong numbers.

   Copy the table and put the statements against the numbers so that every pairing is correct.

| | |
|---|---|
| 0.047 | 4 significant figures |
| 0.003 | 2 significant figures |
| 16.22 | 3 significant figures |
| 184 200 | 2 decimal places |
| 7.06 | 3 decimal places |

# 4.6  Estimating

We can *estimate* the answers to calculations by rounding all the numbers sensibly. We often round to just one significant figure. However, depending on the numbers involved in the calculation, it may be better to round sensibly than to one significant figure.

For example,  $33.78 \div 17.24$  is roughly  $34 \div 17$,  when the numbers are rounded sensibly, giving a simple estimate for the answer of 2.

## Example 1

A box of chocolates costs  £2.72.

Estimate the total cost of 4 boxes of chocolates.

## Solution

(a)   Cost (£)  $= 4 \times 2.72$

   Estimate  $= 4 \times 3$

   $= £12$

> To make sure that you obtain the correct answer when you use a calculator,
>
>> ESTIMATE  the answer mentally,
>>
>> CALCULATE  the answer using your calculator
>>
>> and then
>>
>> CHECK  that the calculator answer is sensible by comparing it with your mental estimate.

## Example 2

Halim uses his calculator to work out  $8.623 \times 4.71$.

He gets the answer  406.1433.

Use an estimate to check his answer.

## Solution

(a)    Estimate  $=\ 9 \times 5$

$=\ 45$

Halim's answer should have been  40.61433.

## Example 3

Jai carries out the following calculations on his calculator, and writes his answers correct to 3 decimal places:

A    $3.62 \times 8.94 = 32.363$

B    $47.92 \div 2.17 = 1.512$

C    $184 \times 3.616 = 665.344$

D    $(21.4 + 19.7) \times 3.61 = 14.837$

Use estimates to decide which answers *could be correct* and which are *definitely incorrect*.

## Solution

A    Estimate  $=\ 4 \times 9$

$=\ 36$

suggesting that Jai's answer *could be correct*.

B    Estimate  $=\ 50 \div 2$

$=\ 25$

showing that Jai's answer *must be incorrect*.

C    Estimate  $= 200 \times 4$

$\qquad = 800$

suggesting that Jai's answer *could be correct*.


D    Estimate  $= (20 + 20) \times 4$

$\qquad = 40 \times 4$

$\qquad = 160$

showing that Jai's answer *must be incorrect*.

 ## Exercises

1.    For each of the calculations listed below,

(i)    *estimate* the answer,

(ii)   use a calculator to *work out* the answer,

(iii)  *compare* your estimate with the answer from the calculator:

(a)    $4.7 \times 8.34$ (b)    $9.6 \times 21.43$ (c)    $11.46 \times 8.02$

(d)    $18.3 \times 108$ (e)    $95 \times 76$ (f)    $15.4 \times 24.9$


2.    Boxes of matches each contain 52 matches.  Estimate the total number of matches in 8 boxes.


3.    The floor of a room measures  3.61 m by 4.72 m.

(a)    *Estimate* the area of the floor of the room.

(b)    *Calculate* the area of the floor, using a calculator.

(c)    *Compare* your estimate with the answer from the calculator.


4.    Estimate the cost of 23 cans of drink costing 37p each.


5.    Kyle uses his calculator to do the calculations listed below, and gives his answers correct to 3 decimal places:

A      $36.41 \times 37.32 = 135.882$

B      $56.2 \times 1.97 = 11.071$

C      $82.3 \times 0.625 = 51.438$

D      $(204 + 109) \times 10.2 = 3.193$

E      $(16.7 + 31.3) \div 4.75 = 1.011$

By using estimates, decide which calculations Kyle has *not* done correctly.

6. Make estimates for each of the calculations below:

(a) $\dfrac{6.1 \times 3.4}{4.2}$

(b) $\dfrac{7.3 + 9.1}{2.3}$

(c) $\dfrac{62.6 \times 21.3}{34.9}$

(d) $\dfrac{71.3 \times 99.6}{11.3}$

(e) $\dfrac{142.3 - 93.6}{23.8}$

(f) $\dfrac{16.5 \times 19.2}{33.6 - 21.9}$

7. Estimate the cost of 18 calculators that cost £7.99 each.

8. A can contains 330 ml of a drink and there are 144 cans in a box. Estimate the total volume of drink in a box, in litres.

9. A car uses 0.18 litres of fuel to travel 1 mile.

(a) *Estimate* the amount of fuel that is used on a 162 mile journey.

(b) *Use a calculator* to work out the amount of fuel that is used.

(c) Does your estimate support the answer from your calculator?

10. Tickets to watch a football match cost £19 each. If 26 472 people watch the match, estimate the total amount that has been paid by these spectators.

## 4.7 Calculator Logic - Bracket and Memory Keys

When using your calculator it is important to be aware of both how it works and how to make the best use of it. Most calculators have *bracket* and *memory* keys that can be used for more complex calculations.

Note: A *scientific calculator* will always try to apply the rules of BODMAS.

Brackets can be inserted at any stage of a calculation by using the bracket keys ⎡(⎤

and ⎡)⎤ . The calculator may show an error message if brackets are not in pairs.

The notation on calculator memory keys varies from one machine to another. You need to find out the keys on your calculator that perform the following functions:

⎡M in⎤ or ⎡STO⎤ places a number on display in the memory.

⎡M +⎤ *adds* the number on display to the number in the memory.

$\boxed{\text{M}-}$    *subtracts* the number on display from the number in the memory.

$\boxed{\text{M R}}$ or $\boxed{\text{RCL}}$   brings the number in the memory to the display screen.

Some of these keys perform other functions in other modes (especially in statistical mode).

One thing you will need to find out for yourself is how to *empty* the contents of the memory; this varies from one calculator to another.

## Example 1

Calculate

$$\frac{6.2 + 8.6}{3.9 - 2.4}$$

correct to 3 significant figures.

## Solution

Using brackets,

$\boxed{(}$ 6.2 $\boxed{+}$ 8.6 $\boxed{)}$ $\boxed{÷}$ $\boxed{(}$ 3.9 $\boxed{-}$ 2.4 $\boxed{)}$ $\boxed{=}$    gives 9.87 to
   3 significant figures

Using the memory,

3.9 $\boxed{-}$ 2.4 $\boxed{=}$ $\boxed{\text{M in}}$

6.2 $\boxed{+}$ 8.6 $\boxed{=}$ $\boxed{÷}$ $\boxed{\text{M R}}$ $\boxed{=}$    gives 9.87 to 3 significant figures

## Example 2

Calculate

$$\frac{6}{3 + 4 \times 7.2}$$

correct to 2 decimal places.

## Solution

Using brackets,

6 $\boxed{÷}$ $\boxed{(}$ 3 $\boxed{+}$ 4 $\boxed{\times}$ 7.2 $\boxed{)}$ $\boxed{=}$    gives 0.1886 . . . = 0.19 to
   2 decimal places

*(Remember that a scientific calculator will apply BODMAS.)*

Using memory,

$$3 \boxed{+} \; 4 \boxed{\times} \; 7.2 \boxed{=} \boxed{\text{M in}}$$

$$6 \boxed{\div} \boxed{\text{M R}} \boxed{=} \text{ gives } 0.1886 \dots$$

$$= \;\; 0.19 \text{ to } 2 \text{ decimal places}$$

## Example 3

Do you need to include brackets if you use a scientific calculator to work out:

(a)    $3 \times 4 + 6 \times 2$                    (b)    $\dfrac{24}{8-2}$ ?

## Solution

(a)     The correct answer is   $3 \times 4 + 6 \times 2 = 12 + 12$

$$= 24$$

Using a scientific calculator without brackets also gives 24, so brackets *are not* needed here.

(b)     The correct answer is   $\dfrac{24}{8-2} = \dfrac{24}{6}$

$$= 4$$

Without brackets the calculator gives the answer 1.

It actually works out   $24 \div 8 - 2$   or   $\dfrac{24}{8} - 2$   which gives 1, so brackets *are* needed here.

## Exercises

1.     Carry out the following calculations using a calculator, giving your answers, where necessary, correct to 2 decimal places:

       (a)    $6 \times (8.7 - 1.05)$               (b)    $\dfrac{2 \times 47}{6 + 9}$

       (c)    $\dfrac{6 + 17}{3}$                       (d)    $\dfrac{42 - 3}{7}$

       (e)    $\dfrac{6 + 22}{47 - 21}$                (f)    $\dfrac{9 - 32}{8 - 27}$

2. Carry out the calculation below.  You may use the memory of your calculator, but not the bracket keys.  Give your answers correct to 3 significant figures.

(a) $\dfrac{4.9}{3.7 \times 2.6}$

(b) $\dfrac{4.7}{16 - 7}$

(c) $\dfrac{9.2 \times 6.7}{4 + 16.2}$

(d) $\dfrac{11.2 - 9.47}{12 - 0.81}$

3. Use brackets or the memory facilities on a calculator to calculate the following, giving your answers, where necessary, correct to 3 decimal places.

(a) $8 + \dfrac{6}{9 + 7}$

(b) $\dfrac{1.9 + 12.2}{8 - 3}$

(c) $\dfrac{6.3 \times 5.32 + 6.49}{(2.94 - 1.62) \times 3.5}$

(d) $\dfrac{21.5}{8 + 3} + \dfrac{6.7 + 3.2}{4.9}$

4. Calculate

$$\dfrac{4.7 \times (5.32 + 6.49)}{(2.94 - 1.62) \times 3.5}$$

(a) correct to 2 significant figures,

(b) correct to 2 decimal places.

5. James tried to calculate $\dfrac{6}{8 + 2}$.  He obtained the answer 2.75, which is wrong.

(a) What is the correct answer?

(b) What did James do wrong?

6. Do you need to use brackets if you work the calculations below out on a calculator, *without* using the memory facilities?

(a) $\dfrac{6}{2} + \dfrac{9}{5}$

(b) $\dfrac{8}{4} + 3 \times 6$

(c) $\dfrac{6 + 9}{2}$

(d) $\dfrac{8 + 3 \times 6}{4}$

7. Calculate $\dfrac{3 + 9 + 17 + 8 + 6 + 9 + 4 + 7}{5 + 3}$ using a calculator, giving your answer correct to:

(a) 2 decimal places,

(b) 2 significant figures.

8.  For each set of instructions given below, write down the calculation that it was used to find:

    (a)  $6 \div ( 8 - 7 + 2 ) =$

    (b)  $4 + 7 \times ( 9 + 4 ) =$

    (c)  $4 \div ( 8 - 5 ) + 6 =$

    (d)  $1 + 7 \times ( 8 - 3 )$
         $\div ( 2 + 9 ) =$

9.  Without using the fraction key, use your calculator to work out the following, giving your answers, where necessary, correct to 3 significant figures:

    (a)  $\dfrac{1}{6} + \dfrac{1}{5} + \dfrac{1}{4} + \dfrac{1}{3} + \dfrac{1}{2} + 1$

    (b)  $\dfrac{1}{\dfrac{1}{6} + \dfrac{1}{5} + \dfrac{1}{4} + \dfrac{1}{3}}$

    (c)  $\dfrac{1}{1 + \left( \dfrac{1}{\left(6 + \dfrac{1}{5}\right)} \right)}$

# 5 Data Analysis

## 5.1 Frequency Tables: Discrete Ungrouped Data

In this section we revise collecting data to draw vertical line graphs or pie charts.

### Example 1

The pupils in Mr Middleton's class take a maths test and get scores out of 10, which are listed below:

| | | | | | | | | | |
|---|---|---|---|---|---|---|---|---|---|
| 3 | 7 | 6 | 2 | 5 | 9 | 10 | 8 | 7 | 1 |
| 8 | 4 | 3 | 5 | 6 | 7 | 8 | 7 | 6 | 5 |
| 3 | 6 | 9 | 8 | 7 | 5 | 9 | 6 | 7 | 8 |

Illustrate these results using a pie chart.

### Solution

First construct a tally chart and then calculate the angles for the pie chart.

| Score | Tally | Frequency | Angle |
|---|---|---|---|
| 1 | I | 1 | $\frac{360}{30} \times 1 = 12°$ |
| 2 | I | 1 | $\frac{360}{30} \times 1 = 12°$ |
| 3 | I I I | 3 | $\frac{360}{30} \times 3 = 36°$ |
| 4 | I | 1 | $\frac{360}{30} \times 1 = 12°$ |
| 5 | I I I I | 4 | $\frac{360}{30} \times 4 = 48°$ |
| 6 | ⧚⧚⧚ | 5 | $\frac{360}{30} \times 5 = 60°$ |
| 7 | ⧚⧚⧚ I | 6 | $\frac{360}{30} \times 6 = 72°$ |
| 8 | ⧚⧚⧚ | 5 | $\frac{360}{30} \times 5 = 60°$ |
| 9 | I I I | 3 | $\frac{360}{30} \times 3 = 36°$ |
| 10 | I | 1 | $\frac{360}{30} \times 1 = 12°$ |

TOTAL 30                                360°

The pie chart can now be drawn as shown below:

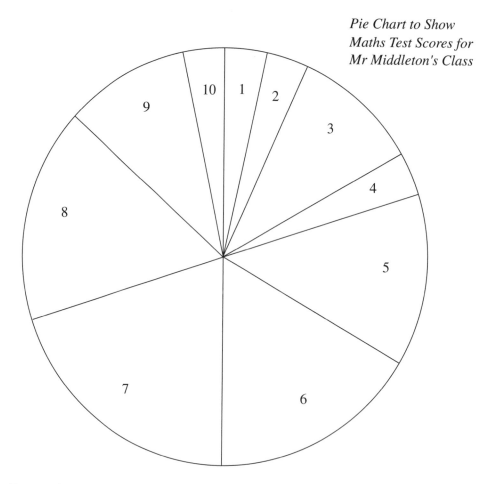

*Pie Chart to Show*
*Maths Test Scores for*
*Mr Middleton's Class*

Note: Remember to always give a title for the pie chart.

## Example 2

Mrs Panni gave her class the same maths test as Mr Middleton's class in
Example 1. The scores for her class are given below:

| 3 | 4 | 4 | 4 | 5 | 6 | 7 | 7 | 4 | 3 |
|---|---|---|---|---|---|---|---|---|---|
| 5 | 7 | 6 | 7 | 5 | 8 | 3 | 5 | 6 | 4 |
| 6 | 7 | 7 | 6 | 6 | 4 | 6 | 5 | 6 | 7 |

Draw vertical line graphs for *both* classes and comment on the differences that
they show.

## Solution

First construct a tally chart for Mrs Panni's class.

| Score | Tally | Frequency |
|-------|-------|-----------|
| 1 | | 0 |
| 2 | | 0 |
| 3 | I I I | 3 |
| 4 | IIII I | 6 |
| 5 | IIII | 5 |
| 6 | IIII I I I | 8 |
| 7 | IIII I I | 7 |
| 8 | I | 1 |
| 9 | | 0 |
| 10 | | 0 |

The vertical line graph for Mrs Panni's class is shown below:

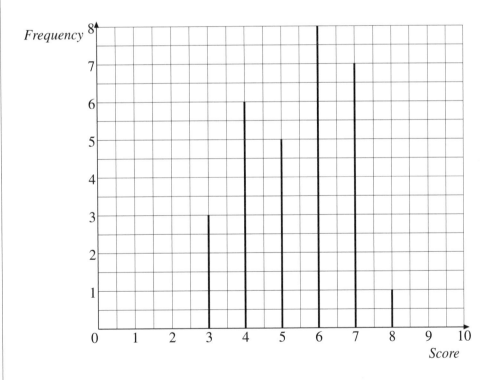

The vertical line graph for Mr Middleton's class is shown below:

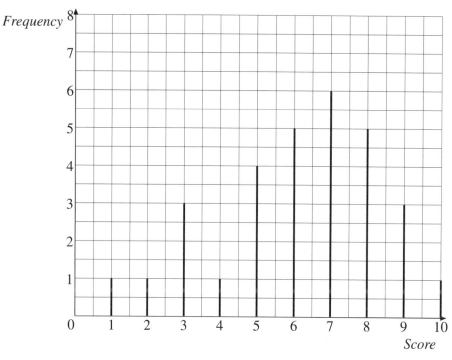

From the graphs we can see that Mr Middleton's class has some pupils who did better than those in Mrs Panni's class, but it also has some pupils who had lower scores.

## Exercises

1.  Emma stops at the park on her way to school every day for 2 weeks to look for conkers. The number of conkers she finds each day is listed below:

    2   10   1   2   3   4   5   3   2   4

    (a)  Draw a pie chart to illustrate these data.

    (b)  Can you think of a possible reason for the unusual number in the data?

2.  Mr Rafiq runs a video library. Over a period of 3 days he notes how many videos have been borrowed during each hour. His records are shown below:

    3   2   4   3   8   7   9   3   10   2

    4   6   8   4   12   10   8   5   6   4

    3   2   6   9   4   5   7   6   5   7

    (a)  Draw a pie chart to illustrate these data.

    (b)  What was the *largest* number of videos hired in any hour?

    (c)  What was the *least* number of videos hired in any hour?

    (d)  What was the *most common* number of videos hired in any hour?

3.  The total number of goals scored in each of the Premier League matches one Saturday were:

    0   1   0   4   5   4   2   3   1   4

    (a)   Illustrate these data on a pie chart.

    (b)   Which number of goals was the most common?

4.  The pie chart below illustrates the scores obtained on a maths test by a class of 24 pupils:

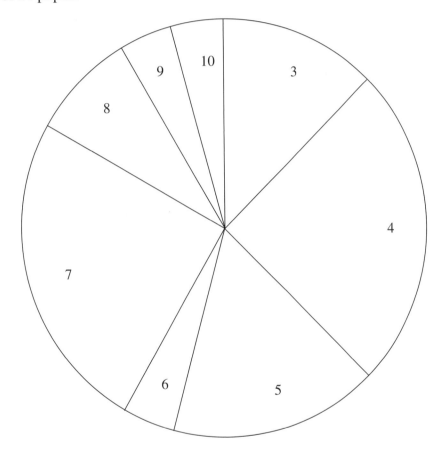

    (a)   How many degrees represent each pupil?

    (b)   How many pupils get each score?

5.  The National Curriculum levels reached in maths by a class at Key Stage 3 were:

    6   5   6   4   3   4   4   5   6   4   5   6   6   5

    5   6   4   4   6   6   5   5   6   4   6   5   4   5

    (a)   Draw a vertical line diagram for this data.

    (b)   Which level was obtained by most pupils?

6. The class in question 5 were also given National Curriculum levels for English and these are listed below:

6 4 5 3 4 3 4 6 5 4 6 5 5 6

4 6 4 5 5 5 4 5 5 3 6 4 4 4

(a) Draw a vertical line graph for the data.

(b) Compare this graph with the one for question 5 and comment on any differences.

7. A calculator was used to produce 40 random digits. These are listed below:

7 2 1 0 5 4 6 8 1 2

9 9 2 1 0 3 5 3 7 6

5 4 1 0 9 3 9 9 4 5

6 7 8 0 1 2 3 9 7 1

(a) Draw a vertical line graph to illustrate this data.

(b) Do you think that the calculator is good at producing random numbers? How does the graph support your answer?

8. A train company keeps a daily record of the number of trains that were late for two different months and these data are shown below:

*January* 1 0 2 7 3 1 2 4 5 1 2

4 7 4 3 0 1 4 1 3 2 1

2 3 4 5 6 0 1 2 9

*February* 5 6 5 4 3 7 8 1 4 3 4

5 6 4 3 4 2 6 4 8 9 5

3 4 3 5 4 4

(a) Draw a vertical line graph for each month.

(b) In which month was the better service provided to passengers?

(c) Why is the amount of data different for each of the two months?

(d) If January had the same number of days as February, would your answer to (b) be the same?

9.  Peter grows tomatoes in his greenhouse. During August he keeps records of the number of tomatoes he picks each day. The results for 1997 and 1998 are shown below:

| 1997 | 6 | 7 | 8 | 10 | 12 | 14 | 10 | 15 | 12 | 9 | 6 |
|------|----|----|----|----|----|----|----|----|----|----|----|
|      | 8 | 10 | 8 | 7 | 9 | 16 | 20 | 19 | 12 | 10 | 11 |
|      | 12 | 10 | 9 | 8 | 7 | 9 | 11 | 12 | 8 |   |   |
| 1998 | 11 | 11 | 14 | 16 | 15 | 12 | 12 | 11 | 8 | 9 | 20 |
|      | 19 | 17 | 18 | 19 | 15 | 16 | 17 | 15 | 12 | 11 | 10 |
|      | 8 | 17 | 18 | 20 | 15 | 16 | 17 | 19 | 15 |   |   |

(a)  Draw vertical line graphs for each year.

(b)  Describe how the two years compare.

# 5.2  Mean, Median, Mode and Range

The *mean, median* and *mode* are types of average.
The *range* gives a measure of the *spread* of a set of data.

| *Definition* | *Example* |
|---|---|
| $Mean = \dfrac{\text{sum of all data}}{\text{number of values}}$ | For 1, 2, 2, 3, 4 <br><br> $\begin{aligned} Mean &= \dfrac{1+2+2+3+4}{5} \\[4pt] &= \dfrac{12}{5} \\[4pt] &= 2.4 \end{aligned}$ |
| $Mode = $ most common value | For 1, 2, 2, 3, 4 <br> $Mode = 2$ <br><br> For 1, 2, 2, 3, 4, 4, 5 <br> $Mode = 2$ and 4 |
| $Median = $ middle value when data is arranged in order | For 1, 2, (2,) 3, 4 <br> $Median = 2$ <br><br> For 1, 2, (2, 3,) 4, 4 <br> $Median = \dfrac{2+3}{2}$ <br> $= 2.5$ |

| *Definition* | *Example* |
|---|---|
| *Range* = largest value – smallest value | For 1, 2, 2, 3, 4 |
| | *Range* = 4 – 1 |
| | = 3 |

The *mean, median, mode* and *range* can also be calculated when the data is presented in the form of a frequency table.

## Example 1

For the data presented in the table opposite, calculate:

(a)    the *mode*,

(b)    the *range*,

(c)    the *median*,

(d)    the *mean*.

| Score | Frequency |
|---|---|
| 0 | 2 |
| 1 | 6 |
| 2 | 12 |
| 3 | 4 |
| 4 | 1 |

## Solution

(a)    The mode is the most common score.  In this case,

mode  =  2

(b)    Largest score = 4,   smallest score = 0,

range  =  4 – 0

=  4

(c)    The median is the middle value.  As there are 25 scores, the middle value is the 13th score (12 above and 12 below).

When in order:

the first 2 values are  0,

the next 6 values are 1,

therefore the 3rd to 8th values are 1.

The next 12 values are 2,

therefore the 9th to 20th values are 2.

The 13th value is in this group,

so the 13th value is 2.

So the median  =  2

(d)   To calculate the mean, complete a table like the one below:

| Score | Frequency | Score × Frequency | |
|:---:|:---:|:---:|:---:|
| 0 | 2 | 0 × 2  =   0 | |
| 1 | 6 | 1 × 6  =   6 | |
| 2 | 12 | 2 × 12  =  24 | Twelve pupils scored 2, a total of 24 |
| 3 | 4 | 3 × 4  =  12 | |
| 4 | 1 | 4 × 1  =   4 | |
| Totals | 25 | 46 | |

Total number of pupils

Total of the scores

$$\text{Mean} = \frac{46}{25}$$

$$= 1.84$$

## Example 2

Calculate the *mean* and *median* for the data in the table opposite.

| Price | Frequency |
|:---:|:---:|
| 30p | 1 |
| 31p | 3 |
| 32p | 4 |
| 33p | 8 |
| 34p | 2 |
| 35p | 2 |

## Solution

(a)   To calculate the mean, construct a table like the one below:

| Price (pence) | Frequency | Price × Frequency |
|:---:|:---:|:---:|
| 30 | 1 | 30 × 1  =   30 |
| 31 | 3 | 31 × 3  =   93 |
| 32 | 4 | 32 × 4  =  128 |
| 33 | 8 | 33 × 8  =  264 |
| 34 | 2 | 34 × 2  =   68 |
| 35 | 2 | 35 × 2  =   70 |
| Totals | 20 | 653 |

$$\text{Mean} = \frac{653}{20}$$

$$= 32.65\text{p}$$

As there are 20 values, the median will be between the 10th and 11th values.

When in order:

  1st value is 30p

  Next 3 values are 31p

    So the 2nd to 4th values are 31p.

  Next 4 values are 32p

    So the 5th to 8th values are 32p

  Next 8 values are 33p

    So 9th to 17th values are 33p.

So both the 10th and 11th values are 33p.

Median  = 33p

Note: If the 10th and 11th values had been different from one another, we would have used a value halfway between them (the mean of the two numbers).

---

The symbol $\Sigma$ (Greek 'sigma') means 'the sum of' or 'the total of'.
So,

$$\text{mean} = \frac{\Sigma \text{ frequency} \times \text{value}}{\Sigma \text{ frequnecy}}$$

Sometimes we use $f$ to stand for frequency, $x$ for the values and $\bar{x}$ for the mean, so that,

$$\bar{x} = \frac{\Sigma f x}{\Sigma f}$$

---

# Exercises

1.  Calculate the *mean, median, mode* and *range* for each set of data below:

    (a)  3,  6,  3,  7,  4,  3,  9

    (b)  11,  10,  12,  12,  9,  10,  14,  12,  9

    (c)  6,  9,  10,  7,  8,  5

    (d)  2,  9,  7,  3,  5,  5,  6,  5,  4,  9.

2.   (a)   Copy and complete the table below:

| Score | Frequency | Score × Frequency |
|:---:|:---:|:---:|
| 0 | 2 | |
| 1 | 6 | |
| 2 | 8 | |
| 3 | 3 | |
| 4 | 0 | |
| 5 | 1 | |
| Totals | | |

   (b)   Calculate the mean score.

3.   The number of goals scored by a hockey team in each match of a season is listed below:

| | | | | | | | | | |
|:---:|:---:|:---:|:---:|:---:|:---:|:---:|:---:|:---:|:---:|
| 6 | 2 | 2 | 3 | 1 | 0 | 0 | 1 | 2 | 3 |
| 3 | 5 | 4 | 2 | 0 | 1 | 1 | 0 | 2 | 1 |
| 1 | 1 | 1 | 2 | 1 | 1 | 0 | 2 | 3 | 4 |

   (a)   Copy and complete the table below:

| No. of Goals | Tally | Frequency | No. of Goals × Frequency |
|:---:|:---:|:---:|:---:|
| 0 | | | |
| 1 | | | |
| 2 | | | |
| 3 | | | |
| 4 | | | |
| 5 | | | |
| 6 | | | |
| | | | |

   (b)   Calculate the *mean.*

   (c)   Calculate the *median.*

   (d)   What is the *mode*?

   (e)   What is the *range*?

4. The price of a litre of petrol at some garages was recorded and the results are given in the table opposite:

   Calculate the *mean, median* and *mode* of these data.

| Price | Frequency |
|-------|-----------|
| 74p | 1 |
| 75p | 2 |
| 76p | 8 |
| 77p | 10 |
| 78p | 2 |
| 79p | 1 |
| 80p | 1 |

5. A class collected data on the number of children in their families, and this information is listed below:

   | | | | | | | | | | |
   |---|---|---|---|---|---|---|---|---|---|
   | 2 | 1 | 3 | 4 | 2 | 5 | 3 | 1 | 2 | 1 |
   | 1 | 1 | 2 | 3 | 2 | 2 | 2 | 3 | 4 | 2 |
   | 1 | 1 | 1 | 2 | 3 | 2 | 1 | 1 | 2 | 3 |

   (a) Calculate the *mean* number of children per family.

   (b) Calculate the *median* number of children per family.

   (c) Why are there no 'zeros' ?

6. Professor Baker keeps a record of his golf scores, as shown in the table opposite:

   Calculate his mean score.

| Golf Score | Frequency |
|------------|-----------|
| 70 | 3 |
| 71 | 4 |
| 72 | 4 |
| 73 | 4 |
| 74 | 3 |
| 75 | 2 |

7. A class collected data on their shoe sizes and presented it in the table opposite:

   (a) Calculate the *mean, median* and *mode* for the data.

   (b) Which of the three types of average is the most useful to a shoe shop manager ordering stock?

| Shoe Size | Frequency |
|-----------|-----------|
| 3 | 2 |
| 4 | 7 |
| 5 | 6 |
| 6 | 5 |
| 7 | 3 |
| 8 | 2 |

8.  Fataimenta sells vacuum cleaners and the table shows how many she sells each day in a 25-day period.

    (a) Calculate the *mean, median* and *mode* for the data.

    (b) Which of the averages gives the *best* impression of her sales figures?

| No. Sold per Day | Frequency |
|:---:|:---:|
| 0 | 2 |
| 1 | 6 |
| 2 | 6 |
| 3 | 2 |
| 4 | 8 |
| 5 | 1 |

9.  Classes 8A and 8B have a sponsored spelling competition.

    The tables below give the number of correct spellings for both classes.

*Class A*

| No. of Correct Spellings | Frequency |
|:---:|:---:|
| 1 | 0 |
| 2 | 1 |
| 3 | 1 |
| 4 | 1 |
| 5 | 1 |
| 6 | 6 |
| 7 | 5 |
| 8 | 6 |
| 9 | 1 |
| 10 | 3 |

*Class B*

| No. of Correct Spellings | Frequency |
|:---:|:---:|
| 1 | 0 |
| 2 | 1 |
| 3 | 1 |
| 4 | 5 |
| 5 | 2 |
| 6 | 3 |
| 7 | 1 |
| 8 | 2 |
| 9 | 4 |
| 10 | 6 |

    (a) Calculate the *mean, median* and *mode* for each class.

    (b) Which average makes class A appear to be better at spelling?

    (c) Which average makes class B appear to be better at spelling?

10. Paul and David play golf. The scores for their last 20 matches are given below:

| Score | 67 | 68 | 69 | 70 | 71 | 72 | 73 | 74 | 75 | 76 | 77 | 78 |
|:---|:---:|:---:|:---:|:---:|:---:|:---:|:---:|:---:|:---:|:---:|:---:|:---:|
| *Paul's Frequency* | 1 | 1 | 1 | 1 | 2 | 5 | 1 | 2 | 3 | 1 | 1 | 1 |
| *David's Frequency* | 0 | 0 | 3 | 6 | 2 | 0 | 0 | 0 | 0 | 2 | 4 | 3 |

    Produce arguments, supported by an average for each player, to show that each could be considered the better player.

# 6 Nets and Surface Area

## 6.1 Common 2-D and 3-D Shapes

You have already met many 2-D shapes; here are some with which you should already be familiar:

| NAME | ILLUSTRATION | NOTES |
|------|-------------|-------|
| Circle | | Symmetric about any diameter |
| Triangle | | 3 straight sides |
| Equilateral Triangle | | 3 equal sides and 3 equal angles ( = 60 °) |
| Isosceles Triangle | | 2 equal sides and 2 equal angles |
| Right-angled Triangle | | One angle = 90 ° |
| Quadrilateral | | 4 straight sides |
| Square | | 4 equal sides and 4 right angles |
| Rectangle | | Opposite sides equal and 4 right angles |
| Rhombus | | 4 equal sides; opposite sides parallel |
| Trapezium | | One pair of opposite sides parallel |
| Parallelogram | | Both pairs of opposite sides equal and parallel |
| Kite | | Two pairs of adjacent sides equal |

| NAME | ILLUSTRATION | NOTES |
|---|---|---|
| Pentagon | | 5 sides (equal if *regular*) |
| Hexagon | | 6 sides (equal if *regular*) |
| Octagon | | 8 sides (equal if *regular*) |

There are also several 3-D shapes with which you should be familiar:

| | | |
|---|---|---|
| Cube | | All side lengths equal (square faces), and all angles right angles |
| Cuboid | | Faces are combination of rectangles (and squares); all angles right angles |
| Cylinder | | Circular base |
| Sphere | | All points on surface equidistant from centre |
| Pyramid (square-based) | | All slant edges are equal in length in a right pyramid |
| Prism (triangular) | | Cross-section remains the same throughout |
| Tetrahedron | | All four faces are triangular |

Note that a *square* is a special case of a rectangle, as it satisfies the definition; similarly, both a square and a rectangle are special cases of a parallelogram, etc.

## Example 1

What is the name of the 2-D shape with 4 sides and with opposite angles equal?

### Solution

The shape has to be a parallelogram.

(Note: this shape can also be a square, rhombus or rectangle as these are all special cases of a parallelogram.)

## Example 2

Draw accurately:

(a)    a rhombus with sides of length 4 cm and one angle 120 °,

(b)    a kite with sides of length 3 cm and 4 cm, and smallest angle 60 °. Measure the size of each of the other angles.

### Solution

(a)

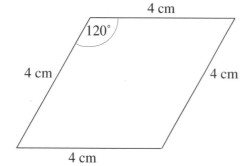

(b)    Note that the smallest angle, 60 °, must be between the two longest sides. The other angles are approximately 108 °, 108 ° and 84 °.

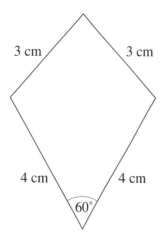

## Exercises

1.  What could be the name of the 2-dimensional shape with 4 sides, which has all angles of equal sizes?

2.  What is the name of a 6-sided, 2-dimensional shape which has sides of equal lengths?

3.  Draw a parallelogram with sides of lengths 3 cm and 4 cm and with smallest angle equal to 60°.

4.  Can a 4-sided, 2-dimensional shape have 4 sides of equal lengths, and *not* be a square?

5.  Can a 4-sided, 2-dimensional shape have 4 angles of equal size, and *not* be a square?

6.  Name all possible 4-sided, 2-dimensional shapes that have *at least* 2 sides of equal lengths.

7.  Name all possible 4-sided, 2-dimensional shapes that have *at most* 2 sides of equal lengths.

# 6.2  2-D Representation of 3-D Shapes

In this section we explore how to draw 3-D shapes, either on squared paper or on *isometric* (triangular spotty) paper. Examples of each for a 2 cm cube, are shown below :

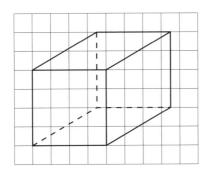
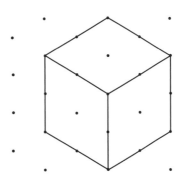

## Example 1

On isometric paper, draw a cuboid with sides of lengths 5 cm, 3 cm and 2 cm.

## Solution

The diagrams below show three of the possible ways of drawing a
2 cm × 3 cm × 5 cm cuboid.

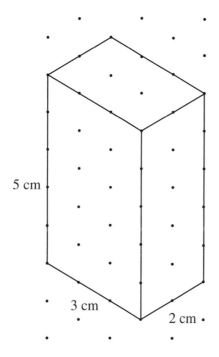

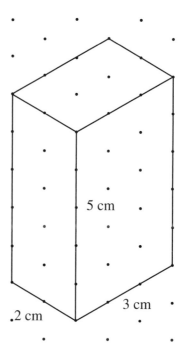

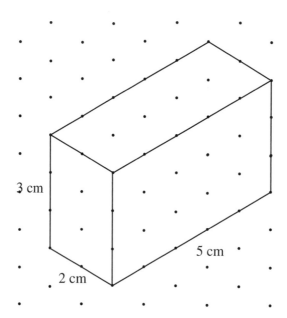

## Example 2

A triangular prism has a cross-section that is a right-angled triangle with base 4 cm and height 5 cm. The length of the prism is 8 cm.

Draw the prism.

## Solution

First draw the cross-section of the prism. Then draw two lines of length 8 cm, parallel to each other. Complete the triangle at the other end of the prism.

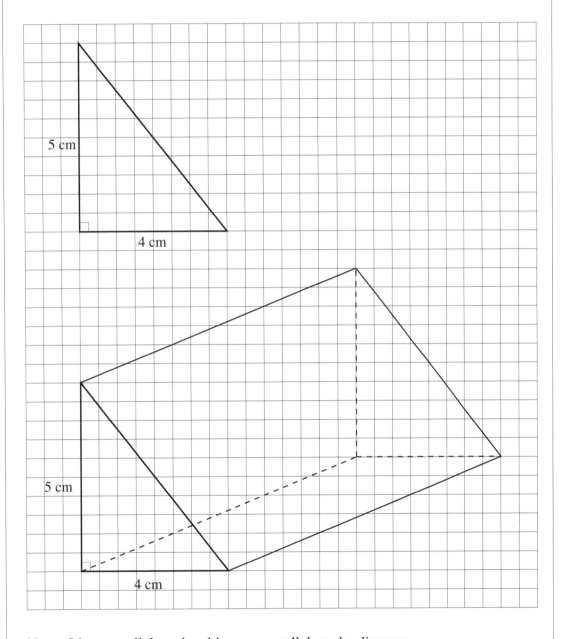

Note: Lines parallel on the object are parallel on the diagram.

## Example 3

Draw this prism on isometric paper:

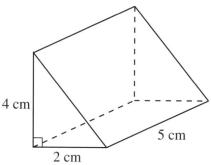

4 cm

2 cm

5 cm

## Solution

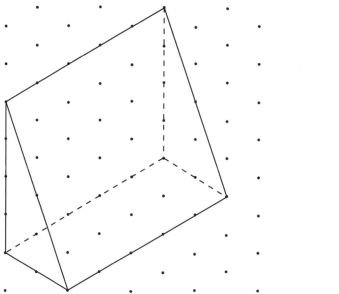

## Exercises

*(Diagrams to be drawn full size unless scale given.)*

1.  On isometric paper, draw a cube with sides of length 4 cm.

2.  On isometric paper, draw a cuboid with sides of lengths 3 cm, 2 cm and 4 cm.

3.  Three cubes with sides of length 2 cm are put side-by-side to form a cuboid. Draw this cuboid on isometric paper.

4.  A cuboid has sides of lengths 3 cm, 6 cm and 2 cm. Draw three possible views of the cuboid on isometric paper.

5.  The cuboid shown in the diagram opposite may be cut in half to form two triangular prisms. Draw one of these prisms on isometric paper.

    Note: *The cut may be made in three different ways.*

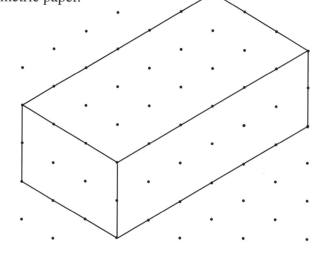

6. A triangular prism has a cross-section that is a right-angled triangle with base 4 cm and height 3 cm. The length of the prism is 6 cm. Draw the prism on isometric paper.

7. On plain or squared paper, draw a cube with sides of 5 cm.

8. On plain or squared paper, draw a cuboid with sides of lengths 6 cm, 4 cm and 3 cm.

9. A prism has a triangular cross-section with sides of length 6 cm. The length of the prism is 8 cm. Draw the prism on plain paper.

10. The diagram shows the cross-section of a triangular prism. The length of the prism is 5 cm.

    Draw the prism on plain paper.

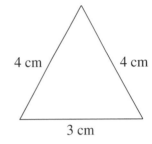

4 cm        4 cm

3 cm

# 6.3  Plans and Elevations

The *plan* of a solid is the view looking *down from above*.

*Side* and *front elevations* are drawn as if looking at the solid from the *side* or the *front*, where the front is taken to be the face nearest to you.

PLAN

RIGHT SIDE ELEVATION

FRONT ELEVATION

## Example 1

Draw the *plan* and *elevations* of this cuboid:

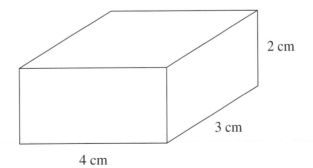

2 cm

3 cm

4 cm

## Solution

The *plan* is the view from above:

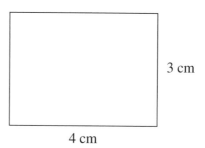

3 cm

4 cm

The *front elevation* is the view from the front:

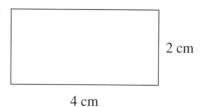

2 cm

4 cm

The *side elevation* is the view from the side
(in this case the right and left side elevations
are the same):

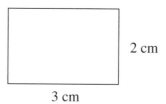

2 cm

3 cm

## Example 2

Draw the *plan, front elevation* and *left side
elevation* for this shed:

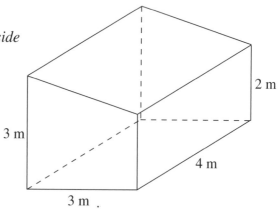

2 m

3 m

4 m

3 m

## Solution

Using 1 cm for 1 m:

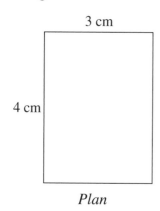

3 cm

4 cm

*Plan*

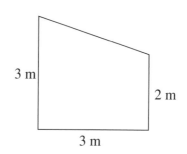

3 m

3 m

2 m

3 m

*Front Elevation*

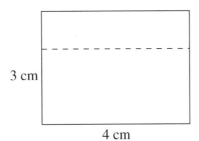

3 cm

4 cm

*Left Side Elevation*

Note: The dotted line on the left side elevation shows the position of the rear roof line which would not be visible from this viewing point.

## Exercises

*(Diagrams to be drawn full size unless scale given.)*

1.  Draw the plan and elevations of the cuboid shown:

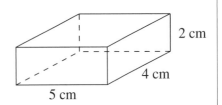

2 cm

4 cm

5 cm

2.  Draw the plan and elevations of the triangular prism shown:

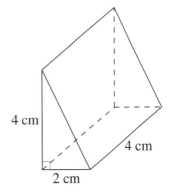

4 cm

4 cm

2 cm

3.  Draw the plan and elevations of the building shown, which is 4 m high:
    Use a scale of 1 cm to represent 1 m.

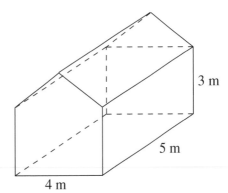

3 m

5 m

4 m

4.  (a)  Draw the plan and elevations
        of the building shown using a
        scale of 1 cm for 1 m:

    (b)  How do these views compare
        with those in Example 2 and
        in question 3 ?

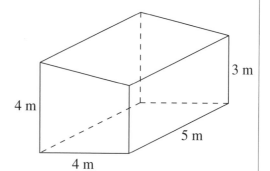

5.  A square-based right pyramid has
    a base with sides of length 4 cm.
    The sides of the pyramid are
    isosceles triangles, and the vertical
    height of the pyramid is 5 cm.
    Draw the plan, and an elevation of
    the pyramid.

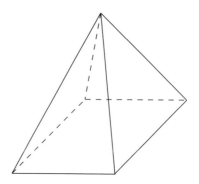

6.  The diagram shows a tissue box.  The opening in the centre of the top of the
    box is 8 cm by 4 cm.

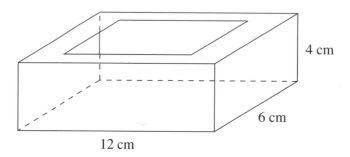

    Draw a plan and elevations of the box.

7.  A hole of radius 1 cm is drilled through the middle of a block of wood as
    shown in the diagram:

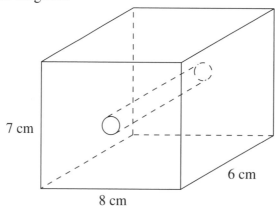

    Draw the plan and elevations of the block of wood.

8.    Draw the plan and elevations of the barn shown
      opposite:

      Use a scale of 1 cm for 1 m.

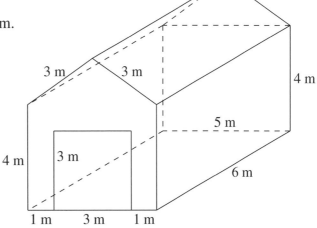

9.    The sketch shows the design of a house with an overhanging roof.

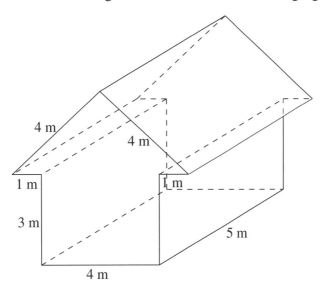

      Draw the plan and elevations of the house.

10.   The diagram shows a factory with a flat roof and a square-based chimney:

      Draw the plan and elevations
      of the building,
      using a scale of
      1 cm for 1 m.

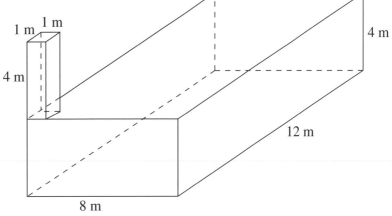

# 6.4 Nets and Surface Area of Cubes and Cuboids

A *net* can be folded up to make a solid. The diagram below shows one of the possible nets of a cube:

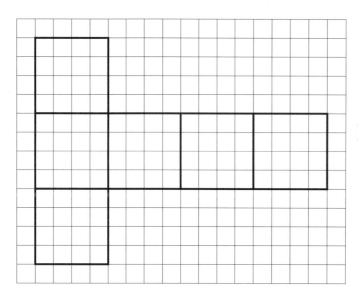

*Diagram to show the net partially folded*

The net of a cube is always made up of 6 squares. Each square has an area of $x^2$ if the length of the side of the cube is $x$.

Total surface area of a cube $= 6x^2$.

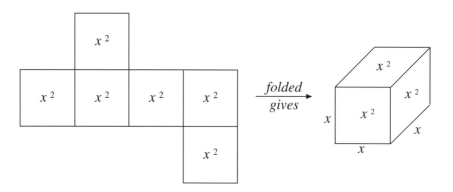

## Example 1

Draw a net for the cube shown and calculate its surface area.

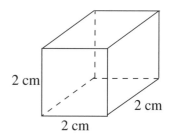

## Solution

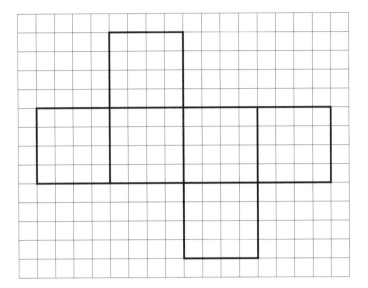

The net is made up of 6 squares.

Each square has an area of 4 cm$^2$.

$$\text{Surface area} = 6 \times 4$$

$$= 24 \text{ cm}^2.$$

---

The net of a cuboid is made up of 6 rectangles.

The rectangles will occur in pairs as illustrated below:

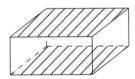 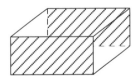 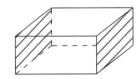

*Top and bottom*  *Two sides*  *Two ends*

For this cuboid,

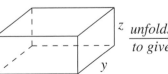

| | $yz$ |
|---|---|
| $xz$  $xy$  $xz$ | $xy$ |
| | $yz$ |

$z$ *unfolds to give*

and, surface area $= xy + yz + xz + xy + yz + xz$

$$= 2xy + 2yz + 2xz$$

$$= 2(xy + yz + xz)$$

## Example 2

Draw a net for the cuboid shown and calculate
its surface area.

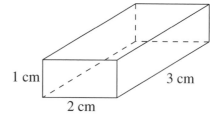

## Solution

One of the possible nets for
the cuboid is shown opposite, together
with the area of each rectangle:

Surface area  $=$  $2 + 6 + 3 + 6 + 3 + 2$

$=$  $22$  cm$^2$

You can check your solution:

$x = 2$ cm,  $y = 3$ cm and $z = 1$ cm
so, using the formula  $2(xy + yz + xz)$,

surface area  $=$  $2(2 \times 3 + 3 \times 1 + 2 \times 1)$

$=$  $2 \times 11$

$=$  $22$  cm$^2$  (as before)

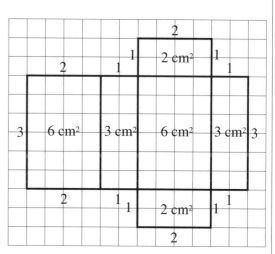

*Side lengths in cm*

## Example 3

Calculate the surface area of this cuboid:

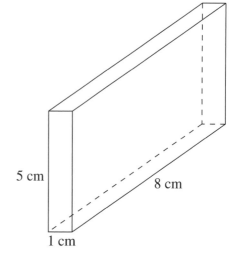

## Solution

Surface area  $=$  $2(5 \times 1 + 1 \times 8 + 5 \times 8)$

$=$  $2(5 + 8 + 40)$

$=$  $2 \times 53$

$=$  $106$  cm$^2$

# Exercises

1.    Draw different arrangements of 6 squares and indicate which of them could be folded to form a cube.

2.    Draw a net for a cube with sides of length 4 cm, and calculate its surface area.

3.    Draw a net for the cuboid shown, and calculate its surface area.

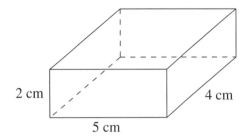

2 cm    5 cm    4 cm

4.    (a)    On card, draw a net for a cube with sides of length 5 cm.

      (b)    Add tabs to the net so that it can be cut out and glued together.

      (c)    Cut out the net, fold it up and glue it together to make a cube.

5.    Use card to make a net for the cuboid shown.

      Then add tabs, cut it out, fold it up and glue it to make the cuboid.

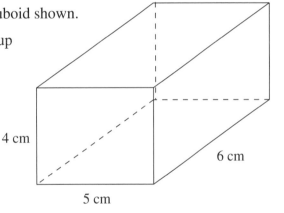

4 cm    5 cm    6 cm

6.    (a)    Draw 2 different nets for the cuboid shown.

      (b)    Calculate the surface area of the cuboid.

      (c)    Do both your nets have the same surface areas?

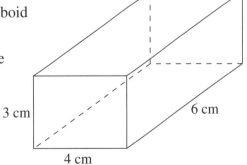

3 cm    4 cm    6 cm

7.    Without drawing a net, calculate the surface area of a cube with sides of length:

      (a)    10 cm          (b)    9 cm.

8.    Calculate the surface area of each of the following cuboids:

(a)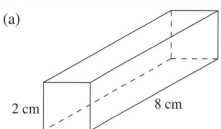

(b)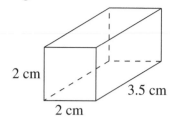

(c)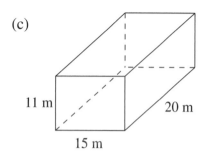

(d)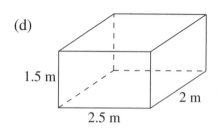

9.    A diagram of a net is shown below, where two of the rectangles have been drawn inaccurately.

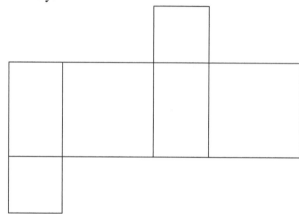

(a)    Explain what is wrong with the net.

(b)    Draw a modified net that would produce a cuboid, by changing two of the rectangles.

(c)    Give an alternative answer to part (b).

10.   The surface area of a cube is 24 cm². Calculate the length of the sides of the cube.

11.   The surface area of this cuboid is 102 cm².
      What is the length marked $x$ ?

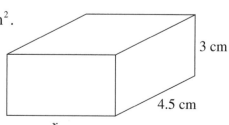

# 6.5  Nets of Prisms and Pyramids

In order to draw the nets of some prisms and pyramids, you will need to construct triangles as well as squares and rectangles.

## Example 1

(a)  Draw a net for this triangular prism:

(b)  Calculate its surface area.

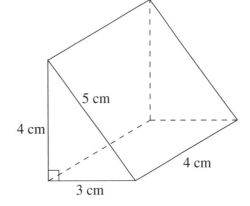

5 cm

4 cm

4 cm

3 cm

## Solution

(a)  A net is shown below where all lengths marked are in cm.

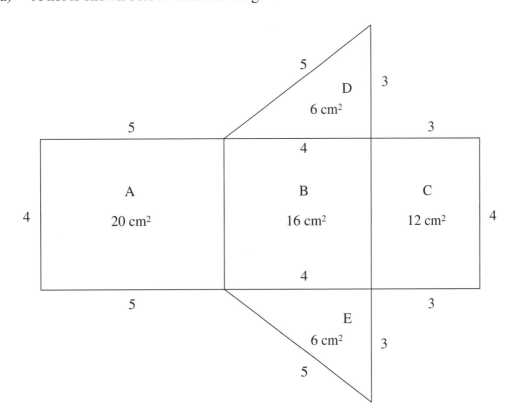

(b)  The area of each part of the net has been calculated.

$$\text{Surface area} = \underset{A}{(5 \times 4)} + \underset{B}{(4 \times 4)} + \underset{C}{(4 \times 3)} + \underset{D}{\left(\frac{1}{2} \times 4 \times 3\right)} + \underset{E}{\left(\frac{1}{2} \times 4 \times 3\right)}$$

$$= \quad 20 \quad + \quad 16 \quad + \quad 12 \quad + \quad 6 \quad + \quad 6$$

$$= \ 60 \ \text{cm}^2$$

## Example 2

The square base of a pyramid has sides of length 4 cm. The triangular faces of the pyramid are all isosceles triangles with two sides of length 5 cm.

Draw a net for the pyramid.

**Solution**

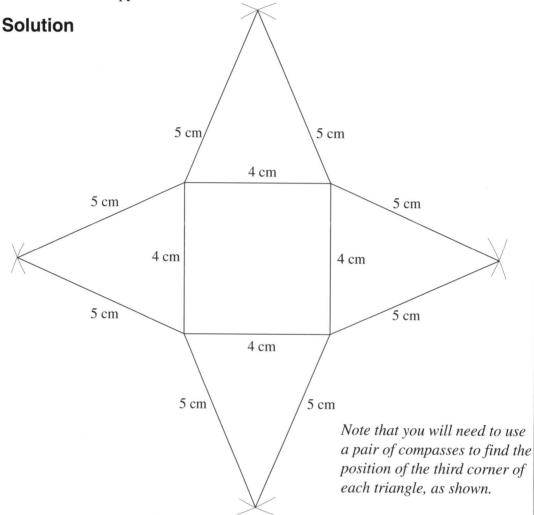

*Note that you will need to use a pair of compasses to find the position of the third corner of each triangle, as shown.*

## Exercises

1.  Draw a net for the triangular prism shown opposite:

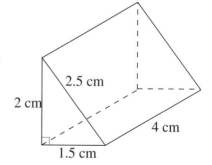

2.

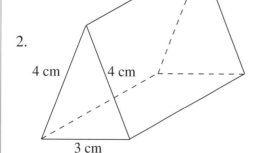

Draw a net for this prism, on card.

Add tabs, cut it out, and then construct the actual prism.

3.    A pyramid has a square base with sides of length 6 cm. The other edges of the prism have length 6 cm. Draw a net for the pyramid.

4.    A pyramid has a rectangular base with sides of lengths 3 cm and 4 cm. The other edges of the pyramid have length 6 cm.

      Draw a net for this pyramid on card, cut it out and construct the pyramid.

5.    A tetrahedron has four faces which are all equilateral triangles. Draw a net for a tetrahedron, which has edges of length 4 cm.

6.    A square-based prism has a base with sides of length 5 cm and vertical height 6 cm. Draw the net of this prism.

7.    The diagram shows a prism:

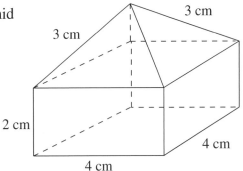

      (a)    Draw a net for the prism.

      (b)    Find the height of the prism.

8.    A container is in the shape of a pyramid on top of a cuboid, as shown in the diagram opposite.

      Draw a net for the container.

9.    The diagram below shows a square-based pyramid; the base is horizontal and AE is vertical. Draw a net for this pyramid.

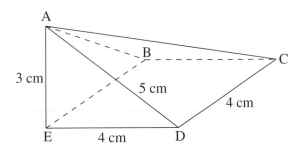

# 7 Ratio and Proportion

## 7.1 Equivalent Ratios

Orange squash is to be mixed with water in a ratio of 1 : 6; this means that for every unit of orange squash, 6 units of water will be used. The table gives some examples:

| Amount of Orange Squash $(cm^3)$ | Amount of Water $(cm^3)$ |
|---|---|
| 1 | 6 |
| 20 | 120 |
| 5 | 30 |

The ratios 1 : 6 and 20 : 120 and 5 : 30 are all equivalent ratios, but 1 : 6 is the *simplest* form.

Ratios can be simplified by dividing both sides by the same number: note the similarity to fractions. An alternative method for some purposes, is to reduce to the form 1 : $n$ or $n$ : 1 by dividing *both* numbers by either the left-hand-side (LHS) or the right-hand-side (RHS). For example:

the ratio 4 : 10 may be simplified to $\frac{4}{4} : \frac{10}{4} \Rightarrow 1 : 2.5$

the ratio 8 : 5 may be simplified to $\frac{8}{5} : \frac{5}{5} \Rightarrow 1.6 : 1$

### Example 1

Write each of these ratios in its simplest form:

(a)  7 : 14  (b)  15 : 25  (c)  10 : 4

### Solution

(a)  Divide both sides by 7, giving

$$7 : 14 = \frac{7}{7} : \frac{14}{7}$$
$$= 1 : 2$$

(b)  Divide both sides by 5, giving

$$15 : 25 = \frac{15}{5} : \frac{25}{5}$$
$$= 3 : 5$$

(c)  Divide both sides by 2, giving

$$10 : 4 = \frac{10}{2} : \frac{4}{2}$$
$$= 5 : 2$$

## Example 2

Write these ratios in the form $1 : n$.

(a)  $3 : 12$  (b)  $5 : 6$  (c)  $10 : 42$

## Solution

(a)  Divide both sides by 3, giving

$3 : 12 = 1 : 4$

(b)  Divide both sides by 5, giving

$5 : 6 = 1 : \dfrac{6}{5}$

$= 1 : 1.2$

(c)  Divide both sides by 10, giving

$10 : 42 = 1 : \dfrac{42}{10}$

$= 1 : 4.2$

## Example 3

The scale on a map is $1 : 20\,000$. What actual distance does a length of 8 cm on the map represent?

## Solution

$$
\begin{aligned}
\text{Actual distance} &= 8 \times 20\,000 \\
&= 160\,000 \text{ cm} \\
&= 1600 \text{ m} \\
&= 1.6 \text{ km}
\end{aligned}
$$

## Exercises

1.  Write each of these ratios in its simplest form:

(a)  $2 : 6$  (b)  $4 : 20$  (c)  $3 : 15$

(d)  $6 : 2$  (e)  $24 : 4$  (f)  $30 : 25$

(g)  $14 : 21$  (h)  $15 : 60$  (i)  $20 : 100$

(j)  $80 : 100$  (k)  $18 : 24$  (l)  $22 : 77$

2.  Write in the form $1 : n$, each of the following ratios:

(a)  $2 : 5$  (b)  $5 : 3$  (c)  $10 : 35$

(d)  $2 : 17$  (e)  $4 : 10$  (f)  $8 : 20$

(g)  $6 : 9$  (h)  $15 : 12$  (i)  $5 : 12$

3.  Write in the form $n : 1$, each of the following ratios:

    (a)   24 : 3          (b)   4 : 5          (c)   7 : 10

    (d)   15 : 2          (e)   18 : 5          (f)   6 : 5

4.  Jennifer mixes 600 ml of orange juice with 900 ml of apple juice to make a fruit drink.  Write the ratio of orange juice to apple juice in its simplest form.

5.  A builder mixes 10 shovels of cement with 25 shovels of sand.  Write the ratio of cement to sand:

    (a)   in its simplest form,

    (b)   in the form  $1 : n$,

    (c)   in the form  $n : 1$,

6.  In a cake recipe, 300 grams of butter are mixed with 800 grams of flour. Write the ratio of butter to flour:

    (a)   in its simplest form,

    (b)   in the form $1 : n$,

    (c)   in the form  $n : 1$.

7.  In a school there are 850 pupils and 40 teachers.  Write the ratio of teachers to pupils:

    (a)   in its simplest form,          (b)   in the form  $1 : n$.

8.  A map is drawn with a scale of  1 : 50 000.  Calculate the actual distances, in km, that the following lengths on the map represent:

    (a)   2 cm          (b)   9 cm          (c)   30 cm.

9.  A map has a scale of  1 : 200 000.  The distance between two towns is 60 km.  How far apart are the towns on the map?

10.  On a map, a distance of 5 cm represents an actual distance of 15 km.  Write the scale of the map in the form  $1 : n$.

# 7.2   Direct Proportion

Direct proportion can be used to carry out calculations like the one below:

> If   10   calculators   cost   £120,
>
> then 1   calculator   costs   £12,
>
> and   8   calculators   cost   £96.

## Example 1

If 6 copies of a book cost £9, calculate the cost of 8 books.

## Solution

If 6 copies cost £9,

then 1 copy costs $£\dfrac{9}{6}$

$$= £1.50$$

and 8 copies cost £1.50 × 8

$$= £12$$

## Example 2

If 25 floppy discs cost £5.50, calculate the cost of 11 floppy discs.

## Solution

If 25 discs cost £5.50 = 550p

then 1 disc costs $\dfrac{550}{25}$ = 22p

so 11 discs cost 11 × 22p = 242p

$$= £2.42$$

## Exercises

1. If 5 tickets for a play cost £40, calculate the cost of:

    (a)   6 tickets          (b)   9 tickets          (c)   20 tickets.

2. To make 3 glasses of orange squash you need 600 ml of water. How much water do you need to make:

    (a)   5 glasses of orange squash,

    (b)   7 glasses of orange squash?

3. If 10 litres of petrol cost £8.20, calculate the cost of:

    (a)   4 litres          (b)   12 litres          (c)   30 litres.

4. A baker uses 1800 grams of flour to make 3 loaves of bread. How much flour will he need to make:

    (a)   2 loaves          (b)   7 loaves          (c)   24 loaves?

5.    Ben buys 21 football stickers for 84p.  Calculate the cost of:

    (a)    7 stickers          (b)    12 stickers          (c)    50 stickers.

6.    A 20 m length of rope costs £14.40.

    (a)    Calculate the cost of 12 m of rope.

    (b)    What is the cost of the rope, per metre?

7.    A window cleaner charges $n$ pence to clean each window, and for a house
    with 9 windows he charges £4.95.

    (a)    What is $n$ ?

    (b)    Calculate the window cleaner's charge for a house with 13 windows.

8.    16 teams, each with the same number of people, enter a quiz.  At the
    semifinal stage there are 12 people left in the competition.
    How many people entered the quiz?

9.    Three identical coaches can carry a total of 162 passengers.  How many
    passengers in total can be carried on seven of these coaches?

10.    The total mass of 200 concrete blocks is 1460 kg.  Calculate the mass of
    900 concrete blocks.

# 7.3 | Proportional Division

Sometimes we need to divide something in a given ratio.  Malcolm and Alison
share the profits from their business in the ratio  2 : 3.  This means that, out of
every £5 profit, Malcolm gets £2 and Alison gets £3.

## Example 1

Julie and Jack run a stall at a car boot sale and take a total of £90.  They share the
money in the ratio  4 : 5.  How much money does each receive?

## Solution

As the ratio is  4 : 5, first add these numbers together to see by how many parts
the £90 is to be divided.

$4 + 5 = 9$,  so 9 parts are needed.

Now divide the total by 9.

$\dfrac{90}{9} = 10$,  so each part is  £10.

Julie gets  4 parts  at £10,  giving  $4 \times £10 = £40,$

Jack gets  5 parts  at £10,  giving  $5 \times £10 = £50.$

## Example 2

Rachel, Ben and Emma are given £52.  They decide to divide the money in the ratio of their ages,  10 : 9 : 7.  How much does each receive?

## Solution

$10 + 9 + 7 = 26$  so  26 parts  are needed.

Now divide the total by 26.

$\dfrac{52}{26} = 2,$  so each part is  £2.

Rachel  gets  10 parts  at £2,  giving  $10 \times £2 = £20$

Ben     gets  9 parts  at £2,  giving  $9 \times £2 = £18$

Emma  gets  7 parts  at £2,  giving  $7 \times £2 = £14$

## Exercises

1.  (a)  Divide  £50  in the ratio  2 : 3.

    (b)  Divide  £100  in the ratio  1 : 4.

    (c)  Divide  £60  in the ratio  11 : 4.

    (d)  Divide  80 kg  in the ratio  1 : 3.

2.  (a)  Divide  £60  in the ratio  6 : 5 : 1.

    (b)  Divide  £108  in the ratio  3 : 4 : 5.

    (c)  Divide  30 kg  in the ratio 1 : 2 : 3.

    (d)  Divide  75 litres  in the ratio  12 : 8 : 5.

3.  Heidi and Briony get £80 by selling their old toys at a car boot sale.  They divide the money in the ratio  2 : 3.  How much money do they each receive?

4.  In a chemistry lab, acid and water are mixed in the ratio  1 : 5.  A bottle contains 216 ml of the mixture.  How much acid and how much water were needed to make this amount of the mixture?

5.  Blue and yellow paints are mixed in the ratio  3 : 5 to produce green.  How much of each of the two colours are needed to produce 40 ml of green paint?

6.  Simon, Sarah and Matthew are given a total of £300.  They share it in the ratio  10 : 11 : 9.  How much does each receive?

7.  In a fruit cocktail drink, pineapple juice, orange juice and apple juice are mixed in the ratio  7 : 5 : 4.  How much of each type of juice is needed to make:

    (a)    80 ml of the cocktail,                    (b)    1 litre of the cocktail?

8.  Blue, red and yellow paints are mixed to produce 200 ml of another colour.  How much of each colour is needed if they are mixed in the ratio:

    (a)    1 : 1 : 2,             (b)    3 : 3 : 2,             (c)    9 : 4 : 3 ?

9.  To start up a small business, it is necessary to spend £800.  Paul, Margaret and Denise agree to contribute in the ratio  8 : 1 : 7.  How much does each need to spend?

10.  Hannah, Grace and Jordan share out 10 biscuits so that Hannah has 2, Grace has 6 and Jordan has the remainder.  Later they share out 25 biscuits in the same ratio.  How many does each have this time?

# 7.4  Linear Conversion

The ideas used in this unit can be used for converting masses, lengths and currencies.

## Example 1

If  £1 is worth 9 French francs, convert:

(a)    £22 to Ff,                    (b)    45 Ff to £,                    (c)    100 Ff to £.

### Solution

(a)    $£22 = 22 \times 9$

$= 198 \text{ Ff}$

(b)    $1 \text{ Ff} = £\dfrac{1}{9}$

so    $45 \text{ Ff} = 45 \times \dfrac{1}{9}$

$= \dfrac{45}{9}$

$= £5$

(c)  $100 \text{ Ff} = 100 \times \dfrac{1}{9}$

$\qquad = \dfrac{100}{9}$

$\qquad = £11\dfrac{1}{9}$

$\qquad = £11.11$  to the nearest pence

## Example 2

Use the fact that 1 foot is approximately 30 cm to convert:

(a)  8 feet to cm,　　　　(b)  50 cm to feet,　　(c)  195 cm to feet.

## Solution

(a)  $8 \text{ feet} = 8 \times 30$

$\qquad = 240 \text{ cm}$

(b)  $1 \text{ cm} = \dfrac{1}{30} \text{ feet}$

so  $50 \text{ cm} = 50 \times \dfrac{1}{30}$

$\qquad = \dfrac{5}{3}$

$\qquad = 1\dfrac{2}{3} \text{ feet}$

(c)  $195 \text{ cm} = 195 \times \dfrac{1}{30}$

$\qquad = \dfrac{195}{30}$

$\qquad = \dfrac{13}{2}$

$\qquad = 6\dfrac{1}{2} \text{ feet}$

## Example 3

If £1 is worth $1.60, convert:

(a)  £15 to dollars　　　　　　　　(b)  $8 to pounds.

## Solution

(a)   £15   =   $15 \times 1.60$

=   $24

(b)   \$1   =   $£\dfrac{1}{1.60}$

=   $£\dfrac{10}{16}$

\$8   =   $8 \times \dfrac{10}{16}$

=   $\dfrac{80}{16}$

=   £5

## Exercises

1.   If  £1  is worth  9 Ff, convert:

(a)   £6  to  Fr,

(b)   £100  to  Ff,

(c)   54 Ff  to  £,

(d)   28 Ff  to  £.

2.   Use the fact that 1 inch is approximately 25 mm to convert:

(a)   6 inches  to  mm,

(b)   80 inches  to  mm,

(c)   50 mm  to  inches,

(d)   1000 mm  to inches.

3.   Before 1971, Britain used a system of money where there were 12 pennies in a shilling and 20 shillings in a pound.  Use this information to convert:

(a)   100 shillings  into  pounds,

(b)   8 shillings  into  pennies,

(c)   132 pennies  into shillings,

(d)   180 pennies  into shillings.

4.   Given that a weight of 1 lb is approximately equivalent to 450 grams, convert:

(a)   5 lbs to grams,

(b)   9 lb into grams,

(c)   1800 grams to lb,

(d)   3150 grams to lb.

5.   Use the fact that 1 mile is approximately the same distance as 1.6 km to convert:

(a)   30 miles to km,

(b)   21 miles to km,

(c)   80 km to miles,

(d)   200 km to miles

6.   On a certain day, the exchange rate was such that £1 was worth $1.63. Use a calculator to convert the following amounts to £, giving each answer correct to the nearest pence.

   (a)   $100               (b)   $250               (c)   $75.

7.   The Japanese currency is the Yen (Y). The exchange rate gives 197 Yen for every £1. Using a calculator, convert the following amounts to pounds, giving each answer correct to the nearest pence.

   (a)   1000 Y             (b)   200 Y              (c)   50 000 Y.

8.   A weight of 1 lb is approximately equivalent to 450 grams. There are 16 ounces in 1 lb. Give answers to the following questions correct to 1 decimal place.

   (a)   Convert  14 oz  to  lb.

   (b)   Convert  200 grams  to  lb.

   (c)   Convert  300 grams  to  ounces.

9.   If £1 is worth 2.8 German Marks (DM), and  1 DM is worth 2800 Italian Lira (L),  use a calculator to convert:

   (a)   800 DM  to £,     (b)   10 000 L to  DM,   (c)   50 000 L  to  £.

10.  There are 8 pints in one gallon. One gallon is equivalent to approximately 4.55 litres. Use a calculator to convert:

   (a)   12 pints  to  litres,              (b)   20 litres  to  pints.

   Give your answers correct to 1 decimal place.

# 7.5  Inverse Proportion

Inverse proportion is when an *increase in one quantity* causes a *decrease in another.*
The relationship between *speed* and *time* is an example of inverse proportionality: as the speed increases, the journey time decreases, so the time for a journey can be found by dividing the distance by the speed.

## Example 1

(a)   Ben rides his bike at a speed of 10 mph. How long does it take him to cycle 40 miles?

(b)   On another day he cycles the same route at a speed of 16 mph. How much time does this journey take?

## Solution

(a)  Time $= \dfrac{40}{10}$

$= 4$ hours

(b)  Time $= \dfrac{40}{16} = 2\dfrac{1}{2}$

$= 2\dfrac{1}{2}$ hours

Note: *Faster speed* $\Rightarrow$ *shorter time.*

## Example 2

Jai has to travel 280 miles.  How long does it take if he travels at:

(a)  50 mph,

(b)  60 mph ?

(c)  How much time does he save when he travels at the faster speed?

## Solution

(a)  Time $= \dfrac{280}{50}$

$= 5.6$ hours

$= 5$ hours 36 minutes

(b)  Time $= \dfrac{280}{60}$

$= 4\dfrac{2}{3}$ hours

$= 4$ hours 40 minutes

(c)  Time saved $= 5$ hours 36 mins $- 4$ hours 40 mins

$= 56$ minutes

## Example 3

In a factory, each employee can make 40 chicken pies in one hour.  How long will it take:

(a)  6 people  to make  40 pies,

(b)  3 people  to make  240 pies,

(c)  10 people  to make  600 pies?

## Solution

(a)    1 person   makes 40 pies in  1 hour.

6 people   make 40 pies in  $\dfrac{1}{6}$ hour  (or 10 minutes).

(b)    1 person makes  40 pies in  1 hour.

1 person makes  240 pies in  $\dfrac{240}{40}$  =  6 hours.

3 people make  240 pies in  $\dfrac{6}{3}$  =  2 hours.

(a)    1 person makes  40 pies in  1 hour.

1 person makes  600 pies in  $\dfrac{600}{40}$  =  15 hours.

10 people make  600 pies in  $\dfrac{15}{10}$  =  $1\dfrac{1}{2}$ hours.

## Exercises

1.    How long does it take to complete a journey of 300 miles travelling at:

    (a)    60 mph,              (b)    50 mph,              (c)    40 mph ?

2.    Alec has to travel 420 miles.  How much time does he save if he travels at 70 mph rather than 50 mph?.

3.    Sarah has to travel 60 miles to see her boyfriend.  Her dad drives at 30 mph and her uncle drives at 40 mph.  How much time does she save if she travels with her uncle rather than with her dad?

4.    Tony usually walks to school at 3 mph.  When Jennifer walks with him he walks at 4 mph.  He walks 1 mile to school.   How much quicker is his journey when he walks with Jennifer?

5.    One person can put 200 letters into envelopes in 1 hour.  How long would it take for 200 letters to be put into envelopes by:

    (a)    4 people,

    (b)    6 people,

    (c)    10 people?

6.    A person can make 20 badges in one hour using a machine.  How long would it take:

      (a)    4 people with machines  to make  20 badges,

      (b)    10 people with machines  to make  300 badges,

      (c)    12 people with machines  to make  400 badges?

7.    A train normally complete a 270-mile journey in $4\frac{1}{2}$ hours.  How much faster would it have to travel to complete the journey in 4 hours?

8.    On Monday Tom takes 15 minutes to walk one mile to school.  On Tuesday he takes 20 minutes to walk the same distance.  Calculate his speed in mph for each day's walk.

9.    Joshua shares a 2 kg tin of sweets between himself and three friends.

      (a)    How many kg of sweets do they each receive?

      (b)    How much less would they each have received if there were four friends instead of three?

10.   Nadina and her friends can each make 15 Christmas cards in one hour. How long would it take Nadina and four friends to make:

      (a)    300 cards,

      (b)    1000 cards?

# 8 Algebra: Brackets

## 8.1 Expansion of Single Brackets

In this section we consider how to expand (multiply out) brackets to give two or more terms, as shown below:

$$3(x + 6) = 3x + 18$$

First we revise *negative numbers* and *order of operations*.

### Example 1

Evaluate:

(a)  $-6 + 10$

(b)  $-7 + (-4)$

(c)  $(-6) \times (-5)$

(d)  $6 \times (4 - 7)$

(e)  $4(8 + 3)$

(f)  $6(8 - 15)$

(g)  $3 - (-5)$

(h)  $\dfrac{(-2) - (-3)}{-1}$

### Solution

(a)  $-6 + 10 = 4$

(b)  $-7 + (-4) = -7 - 4$
$= -11$

(c)  $(-6) \times (-5) = 30$

(d)  $6 \times (4 - 7) = 6 \times (-3)$
$= -18$

(e)  $4(8 + 3) = 4 \times 11$
$= 44$

(f)  $6(8 - 15) = 6 \times (-7)$
$= -42$

(g)    $3 - (-5) = 3 + 5$

$\phantom{3 - (-5) } = 8$

(h)    $\dfrac{(-2) - (-3)}{-1} = \dfrac{(-2) + 3}{-1}$

$\phantom{\dfrac{(-2) - (-3)}{-1} } = \dfrac{1}{-1}$

$\phantom{\dfrac{(-2) - (-3)}{-1} } = -1$

When a bracket is expanded, *every term* inside the bracket must be multiplied by the number outside the bracket.  Remember to think about whether each number is positive or negative!

## Example 2

Expand  $3(x + 6)$  using a table.

## Solution

| × | $x$ | 6 |
|---|-----|---|
| 3 | $3x$ | 18 |

From the table,

$$3(x + 6) = 3x + 18$$

## Example 3

Expand  $4(x - 7)$.

## Solution

$4(x - 7) = 4 \times x - 4 \times 7$

$\phantom{4(x - 7) } = 4x - 28$

*Remember that every term inside the bracket must be multiplied by the number outside the bracket.*

## Example 4

Expand  $x(8 - x)$.

## Solution

$$x(8 - x) = x \times 8 - x \times x$$

$$= 8x - x^2$$

## Example 5

Expand $(-3)(4 - 2x)$.

## Solution

$$(-3)(4 - 2x) = (-3) \times 4 - (-3) \times 2x$$

$$= -12 - (-6x)$$

$$= -12 + 6x$$

## Exercises

1.    Calculate:

(a)    $-6 + 17$          (b)    $6 - 14$          (c)    $-6 - 5$

(d)    $6 - (-9)$          (e)    $-11 - (-4)$          (f)    $(-6) \times (-4)$

(g)    $8 \times (-7)$          (h)    $88 \div (-4)$          (i)    $6(8 - 10)$

(j)    $5(3 - 10)$          (k)    $7(11 - 4)$          (l)    $(-4)(6 - 17)$

2.    Copy and complete the following tables, and write down each of the
       expansions:

(a)

| $\times$ | $x$ | 2 |
|---|---|---|
| 4 | | |

$$4(x + 2) =$$

(b)

| $\times$ | $x$ | $-7$ |
|---|---|---|
| 5 | | |

$$5(x - 7) =$$

(c)

| $\times$ | $x$ | 3 |
|---|---|---|
| 4 | | |

$$4(x + 3) =$$

(d)

| $\times$ | $2x$ | 5 |
|---|---|---|
| 5 | | |

$$5(2x + 5) =$$

3. Expand:

(a) $4(x + 6)$

(b) $3(x - 4)$

(c) $5(2x + 6)$

(d) $7(3x - 4)$

(e) $3(2x + 4)$

(f) $8(3x - 9)$

(g) $(-2)(x - 4)$

(h) $(-3)(8 - 2x)$

(i) $5(3x - 4)$

(j) $9(2x + 8)$

4. Jordan writes $3(4x - 8) = 12x - 8$.

Explain why his expansion is *not* correct.

5. Copy and complete the following tables and write down each of the expansions:

(a)

| × | $x$ | $-2$ |
|---|---|---|
| $x$ | | |

$x(x - 2) =$

(b)

| × | $x$ | $-y$ |
|---|---|---|
| $x$ | | |

$x(x - y) =$

6. Copy the following expansions, filling in the missing terms:

(a) $4x(x + 8) = 4x^2 + \,?$

(b) $(-3)(2x - 7) = \,? + 21$

(c) $4x(x - 9) = 4x^2 - \,?$

(d) $6x(x - 7) = 6x^2 - \,?$

(e) $3x(x - y) = 3x^2 - \,?$

(f) $(-4x)(2x + 8) = \,? - 32x$

7. Expand:

(a) $x(x - 7)$

(b) $x(8 - 2x)$

(c) $6x(x + 2)$

(d) $4x(3x - 5)$

(e) $x(x + y)$

(f) $x(4y - 3x)$

(g) $2x(2x + 3y)$

(h) $5x(2y - 1)$

8. Write down expressions for the area of each of these rectangles, and then expand the brackets:

(a)

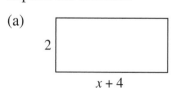

(b)

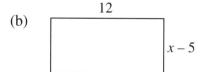

(c)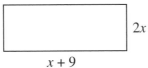

(d)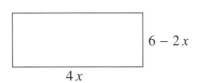

(e)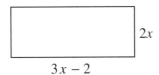

(f)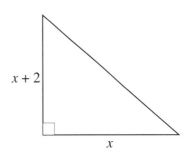

9.  Write down an expression for the area
    of this triangle, that:

    (a)   contains brackets,

    (b)   does *not* contain brackets.

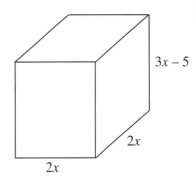

10  Write down an expression for the volume
    of this cuboid, that:

    (a)   contains brackets,

    (b)   does *not* contain brackets.

# 8.2 Linear Equations

Expanding a bracket will usually be the first step when solving an equation like

$$4(x + 3) = 20$$

## Example 1

Solve

$$5(x - 3) = 35$$

## Solution

$$5(x - 3) = 35$$

Expanding brackets gives: $\quad 5x - 15 = 35$

Adding 15 to both sides gives: $\quad 5x = 50$

Dividing by 5 gives: $\quad x = 10$

## Example 2

Solve

$$6(x + 7) = 50$$

## Solution

$$6(x + 7) \;=\; 50$$

Expanding brackets gives: $\qquad\qquad 6x + 42 \;=\; 50$

Subtracting 42 from both sides gives: $\qquad 6x \;=\; 8$

Dividing by 6 gives: $\qquad\qquad\qquad\quad x \;=\; \dfrac{8}{6}$

$$\;=\; 1\tfrac{1}{3}$$

## Example 3

Gilda thinks of a number and adds 7 to it. She then multiplies her answer by 4 and gets 64.

(a)   Write down an equation that can be used to calculate the number with which Gilda started.

(b)   Solve your equation to give the number.

## Solution

(a)   Start with $x$.

Add 7 to give  $x + 7$

Multiply by 4 to give  $4(x + 7)$

This expression equals 64, so the equation is  $4(x + 7) = 64$

(b) $\qquad\qquad\qquad\qquad\qquad 4(x + 7) \;=\; 64$

Expanding brackets gives; $\qquad\quad 4x + 28 \;=\; 64$

Subtracting 28 from both sides gives: $\qquad 4x \;=\; 36$

Dividing by 4 gives: $\qquad\qquad\qquad\quad x \;=\; \dfrac{36}{4}$

$$\;=\; 9$$

# Exercises

1. Solve these equations:

   (a) $2(x + 6) = 14$                 (b) $5(x - 8) = 40$

   (c) $3(x + 5) = 12$                 (d) $7(x + 4) = 42$

   (e) $2(x + 7) = 19$                 (f) $3(x - 4) = 11$

   (g) $5(x - 4) = 12$                 (h) $10(x + 7) = 82$

2. Solve these equations:

   (a) $5(2x - 7) = 8$                 (b) $3(3x + 6) = 27$

   (c) $3(2x + 1) = 30$                (d) $8(2x - 12) = 24$

3. A rectangle has sides of length 3 m and $(x + 4)$ m.

   Find the value of $x$, if the area of the rectangle is 18 m$^2$.

   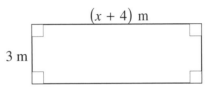

4. Feti chooses a number, adds 7, multiplies the result by 5 and gets the answer 55.

   (a) If $x$ is the number Feti first chose, write down an equation that can be used to determine the number.

   (b) Solve the equation to determine the value of $x$.

5. The following flow chart is used to form an equation:

   $$x \longrightarrow \boxed{+\ 6} \longrightarrow \boxed{\times\ 4} \longrightarrow 17$$

   (a) Write down the equation.

   (b) Solve the equation to find the value of $x$.

6. Solve the following equations:

   (a) $4(7 - x) = 20$                 (b) $3(9 - x) = 15$

   (c) $6(5 - 2x) = 18$                (d) $5(7 - 3x) = 20$

   (e) $2(10 - 3x) = 17$               (f) $6(9 - 5x) = 4$

7.    Alice thinks of a number, subtracts it from 11 and then multiplies her answer by 5 to get 45. What was the number that Alice started with?

8.    Solve the following equations:

   (a)   $2(x + 1) = 6(x - 3)$                    (b)   $3(x + 4) = 11x$

   (c)   $5(x + 4) = 2(10x + 1)$                  (d)   $4(7 - x) = 5(x + 2)$

9.

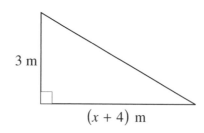

$3\text{ m}$

$(x + 4)\text{ m}$

   (a)   Write down an expression for the area of the triangle.

   (b)   What is $x$ if the area is $15\text{ m}^2$ ?

# 8.3  Common Factors

As well as being able to remove brackets by expanding expressions, it is also important to be able to write expressions so that they include brackets; this is called *factoring* or *factorisation*.

## Example 1

Factorise
$$4x + 6$$

## Solution

First write each term as a product of factors:

$$4x + 6 = 2 \times 2 \times x + 2 \times 3$$

$$4x + 6 = 2(2x + 3)$$

[Note that 2 is the only factor common to both terms and is placed outside the brackets.]

Now you can check your answer by expanding it.

## Example 2

Factorise

$$18n + 24$$

## Solution

$$18n + 24 = (2 \times 3) \times 3 \times n + 2 \times 2 \times (2 \times 3)$$

$$= 6\,(3n + 4)$$

Note that both 2 and 3 are factors of both terms, and so $2 \times 3 = 6$ is placed outside the brackets.

## Example 3

Factorise

$$4x^2 + 6x$$

## Solution

$$4x^2 + 6x = 2 \times 2 \times x \times x + 2 \times 3 \times x$$

$$= 2x(2x + 3)$$

Note that both 2 and $x$ are factors of both terms, and so $2 \times x = 2x$ is placed outside the brackets.

## Example 4

Factorise

$$5x + 20x^2$$

## Solution

$$5x + 20x^2 = 5 \times x + 4 \times 5 \times x \times x$$

$$= 5x(1 + 4x)$$

Note that because 5 and $x$ are factors of both terms, a 1 must be introduced in the bracket when the $5x$ is placed outside the brackets.

You can check the calculation 'backwards':

$$5x(1 + 4x) = 5x \times 1 + 5x \times 4x$$

$$= 5x + 20x^2$$

## Example 5

Factorise

$$3xy^2 + 12x^2y$$

## Solution

$$3xy^2 + 12x^2y = 3 \times x \times y \times y + 3 \times 4 \times x \times x \times y$$

$$= 3xy(y + 4x)$$

Note that $3$, $x$ and $y$ are factors of both terms, and so $3 \times x \times y = 3xy$ is placed outside the brackets.

## Exercises

1.    Factorise:

    (a)   $2x + 4$       (b)   $5x + 15$       (c)   $6x + 18$

    (d)   $5x - 25$     (e)   $3x - 21$       (f)   $7x + 35$

    (g)   $9x - 12$     (h)   $15x + 20$     (i)   $42x + 15$

2.    Factorise:

    (a)   $3x^2 + x$      (b)   $5x^2 + 10$      (c)   $6x - 3x^2$

    (d)   $6x^2 - 4x$     (e)   $21x^2 + 14x$    (f)   $15x - 25x^2$

3.    Denise states that

$$4x + 6x^2 = x(4 + 6x)$$

    (a)   Is her statement true?

    (b)   Describe how it could be improved.

4.    For each statement below, decide if it has been fully factorised and if not, complete the factorisation:

    (a)   $x^2 + x = x(x + 1)$         (b)   $3x^2 + 9x = 3(x^2 + 3x)$

    (c)   $5x - 30x^2 = x(5 - 30x)$    (d)   $8x^2 - 32x = 4(2x^2 - 8x)$

    (e)   $6x^2 - 18x = 3x(2x - 6)$    (f)   $15x - 6x^2 = 3(5x - 2x^2)$

5. Explain why the following factorisation is *incorrect*:

$$15x + 24x^2 = 3x(5 + 24x)$$

6. Factorise:

   (a)   $xy + xz$                 (b)   $xyz + 3yz$

   (c)   $4pq - 8qr$            (d)   $5xyz + 20uxy$

   (e)   $5xy - 4py$             (f)   $7xy + 12xz$

7. Factorise:

   (a)   $x^2 y + xy^2$             (b)   $3x^2 y^2 + 6xy^2$

   (c)   $5x^2 y - 35xy$          (d)   $22xy + 4xy^2$

   (e)   $x^2 yz + xy^2 z$         (f)   $x^2 y - x^3 z$

   (g)   $x^6 y^2 + xy^3$          (h)   $x^4 y^3 + x^2 y^6$

8. (a) Expand    $x(x + y + z)$.

   (b) Factorise    $5x^2 + 2xy + 4xz$.

9. Factorise:

   (a)   $3x + 9y + 18z$         (b)   $4x^2 + 2x + 8xy$

   (c)   $6x - 3xy + 12xz$       (d)   $5xz + 20x - 35xy$

   (e)   $7x^2 + 14xy - 21xy^2$     (f)   $4x + 6xz + 15xy$

10. Factorise:

   (a)   $4x^2 y + 12x^3 y^2 + x^2$     (b)   $6x^7 y^2 - 4x^5 y - x^4 y^2$

   (c)   $3x^2 y^2 - 4xy^3 + x^4 y$     (d)   $5x^7 y - x^2 y^3 + 4x^3 z$

# 8.4 Expansion of Two Brackets

When two brackets are multiplied together, for example,

$$(x + 2)(x + 3)$$

*every* term in the *first* bracket must be multiplied by *every* term in the *second* bracket.

## Example 1

Use a table to determine

$$(x + 2)(x + 3)$$

### Solution

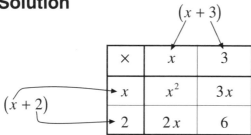

| × | $x$ | 3 |
|---|-----|---|
| $x$ | $x^2$ | $3x$ |
| 2 | $2x$ | 6 |

The multiplication table is formed using the two brackets.

The contents of the table give the expansion.

$$
\begin{aligned}
(x + 2)(x + 3) &= x^2 + 3x + 2x + 6 \\
&= x^2 + 5x + 6
\end{aligned}
$$

or

$$
\begin{aligned}
&\phantom{=}\; x^2 + 3x \\
&\phantom{=}\; \underline{+\, 2x + 6} \\
&= x^2 + 5x + 6
\end{aligned}
$$

## Example 2

Use a table to determine

$$(x - 6)(x + 2)$$

### Solution

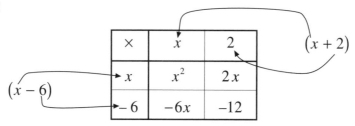

| × | $x$ | 2 |
|---|-----|---|
| $x$ | $x^2$ | $2x$ |
| −6 | $-6x$ | −12 |

So,

$$
\begin{aligned}
(x - 6)(x + 2) &= x^2 + 2x - 6x - 12 \\
&= x^2 - 4x - 12
\end{aligned}
$$

or

$$
\begin{aligned}
&\phantom{=}\; x^2 + 2x \\
&\phantom{=}\; \underline{-\, 6x - 12} \\
&= x^2 - 4x - 12
\end{aligned}
$$

An alternative method for expanding two brackets is shown in the next example.

## Example 3

Determine

$$(x + 2)(x - 7)$$

## Solution

$$(x + 2)(x - 7) = x(x - 7) + 2(x - 7)$$

$$= x^2 - 7x + 2x - 14 \qquad \text{or} \qquad x^2 - 7x$$

$$= x^2 - 5x - 14 \qquad\qquad\qquad\qquad + 2x - 14$$

$$\qquad\qquad\qquad\qquad\qquad = \ x^2 - 5x - 14$$

Note how each term in the first bracket multiplies the whole of the second bracket.

## Exercises

1. Copy and complete the following tables and write down each of the expansions:

(a)

| × | $x$ | 5 |
|---|---|---|
| $x$ | | |
| 4 | | |

$(x + 4)(x + 5)$

(b)

| × | $x$ | − 7 |
|---|---|---|
| $x$ | | |
| 4 | | |

$(x + 4)(x - 7)$

(c)

| × | $x$ | 4 |
|---|---|---|
| $x$ | | |
| − 1 | | |

$(x - 1)(x + 4)$

(d)

| × | $x$ | − 5 |
|---|---|---|
| $x$ | | |
| − 2 | | |

$(x - 2)(x - 5)$

2. Expand:

(a)  $(x + 3)(x + 4)$

(b)  $(x - 2)(x + 5)$

(c)  $(x - 5)(x - 1)$

(d)  $(x + 7)(x - 3)$

(e)  $(x + 2)(x - 3)$

(f)  $(x + 4)(x - 1)$

3.    Expand:

(a)    $(x-1)(x+1)$          (b)    $(x+2)(x-2)$

(c)    $(x-5)(x+5)$          (d)    $(x-7)(x+7)$

How are the answers to this question different from the others you have done?

4.    Explain what is wrong with this statement:

$$(x+5)^2 = x^2 + 25$$

5.    Expand:

(a)    $(x+1)^2$          (b)    $(x-1)^2$

(c)    $(x+3)^2$          (d)    $(x-5)^2$

6.    (a)    Copy and complete this table:

| × | $x$ | 6 |
|---|---|---|
| $2x$ | | |
| 1 | | |

(b)    What is the expansion of

$$(2x+1)(x+6) ?$$

7.    Expand:

(a)    $(2x+1)(2x+4)$          (b)    $(3x+1)(4x+1)$

(c)    $(2x-1)(3x+2)$          (d)    $(4x-1)(5x+1)$

(e)    $(2x+1)^2$          (f)    $(4x-3)^2$

8.    Write out the following expansions, filling in the missing terms:

(a)    $(x+7)(x+6) = x^2 + ? + 42$          (b)    $(x+6)^2 = x^2 + ? + 36$

(c)    $(x-2)(x-5) = x^2 + ? + 10$          (d)    $(x-1)(2x+1) = 2x^2 - x - ?$

(e)    $(x+3)(2x+1) = ? + 7x + 3$          (f)    $(x-7)^2 = x^2 - ? + 49$

9.    Explain what is wrong with this statement:

$$(x+4)(x-5) = x^2 - 20$$

10. Write out the following expansions, filling in the missing terms:

(a) $(x + ?)(x - 1) = x^2 + x - 2$

(b) $(x + 4)(x - ?) = x^2 - 2x - 24$

(c) $(2x + 3)(x + ?) = 2x^2 + 9x + ?$

(d) $(x - ?)(x + 5) = x^2 - 2x - ?$

(e) $(x + ?)(x + ?) = x^2 + 4x + 4$

(f) $(x + ?)(x + ?) = x^2 + 6x + 8$

11. The following example shows how to determine $(x + 1)^3$.

| × | $x$ | 1 |
|---|---|---|
| $x$ | $x^2$ | $x$ |
| 1 | $x$ | 1 |

$$(x + 1)^2 = x^2 + x + x + 1$$
$$= x^2 + 2x + 1$$

| × | $x^2$ | $2x$ | 1 |
|---|---|---|---|
| $x$ | $x^3$ | $2x^2$ | $x$ |
| 1 | $x^2$ | $2x$ | 1 |

$$(x + 1)^3 = (x + 1)(x^2 + 2x + 1)$$
$$= x^3 + 2x^2 + x + x^2 + 2x + 1$$
$$= x^3 + 3x^2 + 3x + 1$$

Use the same method to determine:

(a) $(x + 1)^4$,

(b) $(x + 1)^5$.

Compare your answers with Pascal's Triangle and describe any connections that you see.

# 9 Arithmetic: Fractions and Percentages

## 9.1 Revision of Operations with Fractions

In this section we revise the basic use of fractions.

---

*Addition*

$$\frac{a}{b} + \frac{c}{b} = \frac{a+c}{b}$$

Note that, for *addition* of fractions, in this way both fractions must have the *same denominator.*

*Multiplication*

$$\frac{a}{b} \times \frac{c}{d} = \frac{a \times c}{b \times d}$$

*Division*

$$\frac{a}{b} \div \frac{c}{d} = \frac{a}{b} \times \frac{d}{c}$$

$$= \frac{a \times d}{b \times c}$$

---

## Example 1

Calculate:

(a) $\dfrac{3}{5} + \dfrac{4}{5}$

(b) $\dfrac{3}{7} + \dfrac{1}{3}$

**Solution**

(a)
$$\frac{3}{5} + \frac{4}{5} = \frac{3+4}{5}$$

$$= \frac{7}{5}$$

$$= 1\frac{2}{5}$$

(b)
$$\frac{3}{7} + \frac{1}{3} = \frac{9}{21} + \frac{7}{21} \qquad (common \ \text{denominator} = 21)$$

$$= \frac{16}{21}$$

## Example 2

Calculate:

(a) $\dfrac{3}{4}$ of 48

(b) $\dfrac{3}{5}$ of 32

### Solution

(a) $\dfrac{3}{4}$ of $48 = \dfrac{3}{4} \times 48$

$\qquad\qquad = \dfrac{3 \times 48}{4}$

$\qquad\qquad = 36$

(b) $\dfrac{3}{5}$ of $32 = \dfrac{3}{5} \times 32$

$\qquad\qquad = \dfrac{3 \times 32}{5}$

$\qquad\qquad = \dfrac{96}{5}$

$\qquad\qquad = 19\dfrac{1}{5}$

## Example 3

Calculate:

(a) $\dfrac{3}{4} \times \dfrac{3}{7}$

(b) $1\dfrac{1}{2} \times \dfrac{2}{5}$

### Solution

(a) $\dfrac{3}{4} \times \dfrac{3}{7} = \dfrac{3 \times 3}{4 \times 7}$

$\qquad\qquad = \dfrac{9}{28}$

(b) $1\dfrac{1}{2} \times \dfrac{2}{5} = \dfrac{3}{2} \times \dfrac{2}{5}$ 　　　　or 　　　　$1\dfrac{1}{2} \times \dfrac{2}{5} = \dfrac{3}{{}_1\cancel{2}} \times \dfrac{\cancel{2}^{1}}{5}$

$\qquad\qquad = \dfrac{6}{10}$ 　　　　　　　　　　　　　　　$= \dfrac{3}{5}$

$\qquad\qquad = \dfrac{3}{5}$

## Example 4

Calculate:

(a)  $\dfrac{3}{7} \div \dfrac{3}{4}$

(b)  $1\dfrac{3}{4} \div \dfrac{4}{5}$

## **Solution**

(a)  $\dfrac{3}{7} \div \dfrac{3}{4} = \dfrac{3}{7} \times \dfrac{4}{3}$

$\qquad\qquad = \dfrac{12}{21}$

$\qquad\qquad = \dfrac{4}{7}$

or

$\dfrac{3}{7} \div \dfrac{3}{4} = \dfrac{{}^{1}\cancel{3}}{7} \times \dfrac{4}{\cancel{3}_{1}}$

$\qquad\qquad = \dfrac{4}{7}$

(b)  $1\dfrac{3}{4} \div \dfrac{4}{5} = \dfrac{7}{4} \div \dfrac{4}{5}$

$\qquad\qquad = \dfrac{7}{4} \times \dfrac{5}{4}$

$\qquad\qquad = \dfrac{35}{16}$

$\qquad\qquad = 2\dfrac{3}{16}$

## Exercises

1.  Calculate:

(a)  $\dfrac{1}{7} + \dfrac{4}{7}$

(b)  $\dfrac{3}{8} + \dfrac{7}{8}$

(c)  $\dfrac{1}{9} + \dfrac{7}{9}$

(d)  $\dfrac{3}{10} + \dfrac{1}{10}$

(e)  $\dfrac{7}{13} + \dfrac{9}{13}$

(f)  $\dfrac{6}{7} + \dfrac{5}{7}$

(g)  $\dfrac{5}{7} - \dfrac{3}{7}$

(h)  $\dfrac{7}{9} - \dfrac{4}{9}$

(i)  $\dfrac{11}{13} - \dfrac{6}{13}$

2.  Calculate:

(a)  $\dfrac{1}{2} + \dfrac{1}{3}$

(b)  $\dfrac{1}{5} + \dfrac{1}{7}$

(c)  $\dfrac{1}{4} + \dfrac{1}{5}$

(d)  $\dfrac{2}{3} + \dfrac{1}{2}$

(e)  $\dfrac{7}{8} + \dfrac{3}{10}$

(f)  $\dfrac{3}{4} + \dfrac{4}{5}$

(g)  $\dfrac{3}{7} + \dfrac{2}{3}$

(h)  $\dfrac{4}{9} + \dfrac{2}{3}$

(i)  $\dfrac{1}{4} + \dfrac{5}{8}$

3. Calculate:

(a) $1\frac{1}{2} + 2\frac{1}{2}$      (b) $3\frac{3}{4} + 4\frac{1}{4}$      (c) $2\frac{3}{5} + 3\frac{1}{5}$

(d) $3\frac{1}{3} + 1\frac{1}{2}$      (e) $3\frac{4}{5} + 2\frac{3}{5}$      (f) $5\frac{4}{7} + 3\frac{4}{7}$

(g) $4\frac{3}{4} + 2\frac{5}{8}$      (h) $4\frac{2}{7} + 3\frac{1}{3}$      (i) $2\frac{5}{9} + 3\frac{2}{3}$

4. Calculate:

(a) $2\frac{1}{2} - 1\frac{1}{2}$      (b) $4\frac{3}{4} - 3\frac{1}{4}$      (c) $2\frac{3}{8} - 2\frac{1}{4}$

(d) $4\frac{5}{7} - 3\frac{6}{7}$      (e) $3\frac{5}{8} - 1\frac{7}{8}$      (f) $4\frac{1}{3} - 3\frac{1}{2}$

(g) $2\frac{2}{3} - 1\frac{1}{9}$      (h) $5\frac{3}{7} - 2\frac{1}{2}$      (i) $4\frac{1}{4} - 2\frac{2}{3}$

5. Calculate:

(a) $\frac{1}{4}$ of £20          (b) $\frac{1}{5}$ of 30 kg

(c) $\frac{3}{4}$ of £32          (d) $\frac{4}{5}$ of 90 kg

(e) $\frac{5}{7}$ of 49 kg         (f) $\frac{3}{8}$ of 20 m

(g) $\frac{3}{5}$ of £36          (h) $\frac{7}{10}$ of 42 m

6. Calculate:

(a) $\frac{1}{2} \times \frac{1}{4}$      (b) $\frac{3}{8} \times \frac{1}{5}$      (c) $\frac{2}{3} \times \frac{3}{5}$

(d) $\frac{6}{7} \times \frac{2}{3}$      (e) $\frac{4}{5} \times \frac{3}{4}$      (f) $\frac{4}{7} \times \frac{3}{5}$

(g) $\frac{1}{2} \times \frac{3}{4}$      (h) $\frac{4}{9} \times \frac{3}{7}$      (i) $\frac{1}{8} \times \frac{4}{5}$

7. Calculate:

(a) $\frac{1}{2} \div \frac{1}{3}$      (b) $\frac{3}{4} \div \frac{8}{9}$      (c) $\frac{3}{5} \div \frac{4}{5}$

(d) $\frac{7}{10} \div \frac{1}{2}$      (e) $\frac{3}{4} \div \frac{3}{5}$      (f) $\frac{5}{9} \div \frac{7}{8}$

(g) $\frac{6}{7} \div \frac{2}{3}$      (h) $\frac{4}{7} \div \frac{3}{4}$      (i) $\frac{5}{6} \div \frac{2}{3}$

8. Calculate:

(a) $1\dfrac{1}{2} \times \dfrac{3}{4}$        (b) $3\dfrac{1}{2} \times \dfrac{2}{7}$        (c) $1\dfrac{1}{4} \times \dfrac{2}{3}$

(d) $1\dfrac{1}{2} \times \dfrac{1}{4}$        (e) $2\dfrac{1}{2} \times \dfrac{3}{4}$        (f) $1\dfrac{2}{3} \times \dfrac{4}{5}$

9. Calculate:

(a) $1\dfrac{1}{2} \div \dfrac{3}{4}$        (b) $3\dfrac{1}{2} \div \dfrac{1}{2}$        (c) $2\dfrac{1}{4} \div \dfrac{2}{3}$

(d) $3\dfrac{1}{2} \div \dfrac{1}{4}$        (e) $4\dfrac{1}{2} \div \dfrac{4}{5}$        (f) $3\dfrac{1}{4} \div \dfrac{2}{3}$

10. Calculate:

(a) $1\dfrac{1}{2} \times \dfrac{3}{4}$        (b) $3\dfrac{1}{2} \times 1\dfrac{4}{7}$        (c) $\left(1\dfrac{1}{3}\right)^2$

11. Calculate:

(a) $3\dfrac{3}{4} \div 1\dfrac{1}{2}$        (b) $3\dfrac{1}{2} \div 1\dfrac{1}{4}$        (c) $3\dfrac{1}{3} \div 1\dfrac{3}{7}$

12. Calculate:

(a) $\dfrac{4}{7} + 1\dfrac{3}{4}$        (b) $2\dfrac{1}{2} \times \dfrac{3}{7}$        (c) $5\dfrac{1}{4} - 3\dfrac{1}{6}$

(d) $6\dfrac{1}{2} \div 1\dfrac{6}{7}$        (e) $1\dfrac{1}{2} \times 2\dfrac{2}{3}$        (f) $2\dfrac{2}{3} - 1\dfrac{5}{8}$

# 9.2   Fractions in Context

In this section we consider the use of fractions in various contexts, and how to use the fraction key on a calculator.

## Example 1

There are 600 pupils in a school. How many school lunches must be prepared if:

(a) $\dfrac{3}{4}$ of the pupils have school lunches,

(b) $\dfrac{2}{3}$ of the pupils have school lunches?

## Solution

(a)     $\dfrac{3}{4}$ of $600 = \dfrac{3}{4} \times 600$          or          $\dfrac{3}{4}$ of $600 = \dfrac{3}{\underset{1}{\cancel{4}}} \times \overset{150}{\cancel{600}}$

$\qquad\qquad\qquad = \dfrac{1800}{4}$          $\qquad\qquad\qquad\qquad = 450$ lunches

$\qquad\qquad\qquad = 450$ lunches

(b)     $\dfrac{2}{3}$ of $600 = \dfrac{2}{3} \times 600$          or          $\dfrac{2}{3}$ of $600 = \dfrac{2}{\underset{1}{\cancel{3}}} \times \overset{200}{\cancel{600}}$

$\qquad\qquad\qquad = \dfrac{1200}{3}$          $\qquad\qquad\qquad\qquad = 400$ lunches

$\qquad\qquad\qquad = 400$ lunches

## Example 2

The diagram opposite shows a rectangle.

(a)     Calculate its *perimeter*.

(b)     Calculate its *area*.

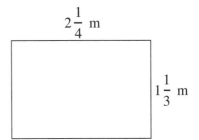

## Solution

$$\text{Perimeter} = 2\tfrac{1}{4} + 1\tfrac{1}{3} + 2\tfrac{1}{4} + 1\tfrac{1}{3}$$

$$= 2\tfrac{3}{12} + 1\tfrac{4}{12} + 2\tfrac{3}{12} + 1\tfrac{4}{12}$$

$$= 6\tfrac{14}{12}$$

$$= 7\tfrac{1}{6} \text{ m}$$

$$\text{Area} = 2\tfrac{1}{4} \times 1\tfrac{1}{3} \qquad\qquad \text{or} \qquad\qquad \text{Area} = 2\tfrac{1}{4} \times 1\tfrac{1}{3}$$

$$= \tfrac{9}{4} \times \tfrac{4}{3} \qquad\qquad\qquad\qquad\qquad = \dfrac{\overset{3}{\cancel{9}}}{\underset{1}{\cancel{4}}} \times \dfrac{\overset{1}{\cancel{4}}}{\underset{1}{\cancel{3}}}$$

$$= \tfrac{36}{12} \qquad\qquad\qquad\qquad\qquad\qquad = 3 \text{ m}^2$$

$$= 3 \text{ m}^2$$

## Example 3

A loaf of bread requires $\dfrac{3}{4}$ kg of flour. How many loaves can be made from $6\dfrac{1}{2}$ kg of flour?

## Solution

$$6\dfrac{1}{2} \div \dfrac{3}{4} \;=\; \dfrac{13}{2} \div \dfrac{3}{4}$$

$$=\; \dfrac{13}{2} \times \dfrac{4}{3}$$

$$=\; \dfrac{52}{6}$$

$$=\; 8\dfrac{4}{6}$$

$$=\; 8\dfrac{2}{3}$$

8 loaves can be made.

Many calculators have a key marked $\boxed{a\,{}^{b}\!/_{c}}$, which can be used to enter fractions.

Pressing 2 $\boxed{a\,{}^{b}\!/_{c}}$ 3 produces the display $\boxed{\;\;2 \lrcorner 3\;\;}$ which represents the fraction $\dfrac{2}{3}$.

Pressing 4 $\boxed{a\,{}^{b}\!/_{c}}$ 7 $\boxed{a\,{}^{b}\!/_{c}}$ 9 produces the display $\boxed{\;4 \lrcorner 7 \lrcorner 9\;}$ , which represents $4\dfrac{7}{9}$.

Note that you must write the fractions in their correct form, and not just copy the display.

(Some calculator displays may be different from this example – check the instruction booklet for *your* calculator.)

## Exercises

1.  Use your calculator to find answers for the following, making sure that they are written in the correct way:

    (a) $\dfrac{1}{4} + \dfrac{3}{7}$     (b) $\dfrac{5}{7} - \dfrac{1}{3}$     (c) $\dfrac{3}{4} \div \dfrac{1}{9}$

    (d) $\dfrac{1}{2} \div \dfrac{1}{6}$     (e) $\dfrac{3}{4} \times \dfrac{7}{8}$     (f) $\dfrac{4}{5} \times \dfrac{3}{8}$

(g) $1\frac{1}{2} \times 7$

(h) $2\frac{1}{2} \times \frac{3}{4}$

(i) $1\frac{5}{7} + 4\frac{2}{3}$

(j) $1\frac{1}{2} \div 1\frac{2}{3}$

(k) $6\frac{1}{4} \div \frac{3}{4}$

(l) $5\frac{1}{2} - 3\frac{2}{5}$

2.  (a)  Enter the fraction $\frac{6}{8}$ and then press the $\boxed{=}$ key on your calculator. Describe what happens.

    (b)  Enter the fraction $\frac{8}{6}$ and then press the $\boxed{=}$ key on your calculator. Describe what happens.

    (c)  What happens to each of the fractions listed below if you enter it into your calculator and then press the $\boxed{=}$ key:

$$\frac{3}{7}, \quad \frac{9}{2}, \quad \frac{4}{6}, \quad \frac{6}{4}, \quad \frac{10}{3}, \quad \frac{3}{10}$$

3.  Calculate the area and perimeter for each of the rectangles below:

    (a)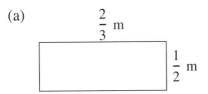

    (b)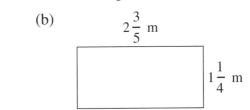

4.  A school has 800 pupils. The Headteacher decides to send a questionnaire to $\frac{2}{5}$ of the pupils. How many pupils receive a questionnaire?

5.  A firm that makes floppy discs knows that $\frac{1}{20}$ of the discs they produce have faults. How many faulty floppy discs would you have if you bought:

    (a)  100 discs,

    (b)  80 discs,

    (c)  2000 discs ?

6.  A cake recipe requires $\frac{3}{8}$ kg of flour. How many cakes could be made with:

    (a)  3 kg flour,

    (b)  6 kg flour,

    (c)  $\frac{2}{3}$ kg flour,

    (d)  1 kg flour,

    (e)  $1\frac{1}{2}$ kg flour,

    (f)  $1\frac{1}{3}$ kg flour.

7.  The rectangle opposite has an area of $2\frac{3}{5}$ cm$^2$.

    What is the length, $x$, of the rectangle?

    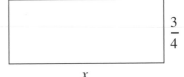

8.  Sheets of paper are $\frac{1}{80}$ cm thick.  Calculate the height of a pile of paper that contains:

    (a)   40 sheets,                    (b)   120 sheets,

    (c)   70 sheets,                    (d)   140 sheets.

    How many sheets would there be in a pile of paper $4\frac{1}{2}$ cm high?

9.  A bottle contains $1\frac{2}{5}$ litres of orange squash.  To make one drink, $\frac{1}{200}$ of a litre of squash is needed.

    How many drinks can be made from the bottle of squash?

10. Calculate the volume of the following cuboid:

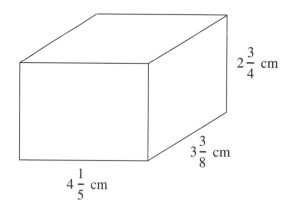

$2\frac{3}{4}$ cm

$3\frac{3}{8}$ cm

$4\frac{1}{5}$ cm

# 9.3   Conversion of Fractions and Percentages

> To convert a *fraction* to a *percentage, multiply* by 100.
>
> To convert a *percentage* to a *fraction, divide* by 100  or  multiply by $\frac{1}{100}$.

## Example 1

Convert the following fractions to percentages:

(a)   $\frac{17}{100}$                  (b)   $\frac{9}{10}$                  (c)   $\frac{3}{5}$

(d)   $\frac{3}{4}$                  (e)   $\frac{1}{3}$                  (f)   $\frac{1}{8}$

## Solution

(a) $\dfrac{17}{100} \times 100 = \dfrac{1700}{100}$

$\qquad\qquad\quad = 17\%$

or $\qquad \dfrac{17}{1\,\cancel{100}} \times \overset{1}{\cancel{100}} = 17\%$

(b) $\dfrac{9}{10} \times 100 = \dfrac{900}{10}$

$\qquad\qquad\quad = 90\%$

or $\qquad \dfrac{9}{1\,\cancel{10}} \times \overset{10}{\cancel{100}} = 90\%$

(c) $\dfrac{3}{5} \times 100 = \dfrac{300}{5}$

$\qquad\qquad\quad = 60\%$

or $\qquad \dfrac{3}{1\,\cancel{5}} \times \overset{20}{\cancel{100}} = 60\%$

(d) $\dfrac{3}{4} \times 100 = \dfrac{300}{4}$

$\qquad\qquad\quad = 75\%$

or $\qquad \dfrac{3}{1\,\cancel{4}} \times \overset{25}{\cancel{100}} = 75\%$

(e) $\dfrac{1}{3} \times 100 = \dfrac{100}{3}$

$\qquad\qquad\quad = 33\dfrac{1}{3}\%$

(f) $\dfrac{1}{8} \times 100 = \dfrac{100}{8}$

$\qquad\qquad\quad = 12\dfrac{4}{8}$

$\qquad\qquad\quad = 12\dfrac{1}{2}\%$

## Example 2

Convert these percentages to fractions:

(a) 30%      (b) 80%      (c) 45%

(d) 6%      (e) $16\dfrac{1}{2}\%$      (f) $62\dfrac{1}{2}\%$

## Solution

(a) $30\% = \dfrac{30}{100}$

$\qquad\quad = \dfrac{3}{10}$

(b) $80\% = \dfrac{80}{100}$

$= \dfrac{8}{10}$

(c) $45\% = \dfrac{45}{100}$

$= \dfrac{9}{20}$

(d) $6\% = \dfrac{6}{100}$

$= \dfrac{3}{50}$

(e) $16\dfrac{1}{2}\% = 16\dfrac{1}{2} \times \dfrac{1}{100}$

$= \dfrac{33}{2} \times \dfrac{1}{100}$

$= \dfrac{33}{200}$

(f) $62\dfrac{1}{2}\% = 62\dfrac{1}{2} \times \dfrac{1}{100}$

$= \dfrac{125}{2} \times \dfrac{1}{100}$

$= \dfrac{125}{200}$

$= \dfrac{5}{8}$

## Example 3

A football team is based on a squad of 20 players. In one season 8 players are shown a red or yellow card.

(a) What percentage of the squad is shown a red or yellow card?

(b) What percentage of the squad is *not* shown a red or yellow card?

## Solution

(a) $\dfrac{8}{20} \times 100 = \dfrac{800}{20}$     or     $\dfrac{8}{1\!\!\not{20}} \times \not{100}^{\,5} = 40\%$

$= 40\%$

(b) $100 - 40 = 60\%$

# Exercises

1. Convert the following percentages to fractions:

   (a) 50%           (b) 75%           (c) 40%

   (d) 25%           (e) 20%           (f) 10%

   (g) 8%            (h) 58%           (i) 36%

   (j) 64%           (k) 76%           (l) 12%

2. Convert the following fractions to percentages:

   (a) $\dfrac{7}{10}$        (b) $\dfrac{1}{2}$        (c) $\dfrac{1}{4}$

   (d) $\dfrac{3}{4}$         (e) $\dfrac{7}{20}$       (f) $\dfrac{6}{25}$

   (g) $\dfrac{19}{20}$       (h) $\dfrac{17}{25}$      (i) $\dfrac{3}{5}$

   (j) $\dfrac{1}{5}$         (k) $\dfrac{11}{20}$      (l) $\dfrac{7}{50}$

3. Convert the following percentages to fractions:

   (a) $12\dfrac{1}{2}\%$     (b) $66\dfrac{2}{3}\%$    (c) $33\dfrac{1}{3}\%$

   (d) $14\dfrac{1}{2}\%$     (e) $18\dfrac{1}{2}\%$    (f) $4\dfrac{1}{4}\%$

4. Convert these fractions to percentages:

   (a) $\dfrac{1}{8}$         (b) $\dfrac{1}{6}$        (c) $\dfrac{3}{8}$

   (d) $\dfrac{47}{200}$      (e) $\dfrac{61}{200}$     (f) $\dfrac{2}{3}$

5. In a class of 25 pupils there are 8 individuals who play in the school hockey team. What percentage of the class play in the hockey team?

6. Halim scores 32 out of 80 in a test. Express his score as a percentage.

7.    An athlete has completed 250 m of a 400 m race. What percentage of the distance has the athlete run?

8.    A double decker bus has 72 seats; there are 18 empty seats on the bus.

   (a)    What percentage of the seats are empty?

   (b)    What percentage of the seats are being used?

9.    Andy buys a bag of 12 apples at a supermarket; there are 4 bruised apples in the bag.

   (a)    What percentage of the apples are bruised?

   (b)    What percentage of the apples are *not* bruised?

10.   Jason took 4 tests at school and his results are given below:

|  |  |  |
|---|---|---|
| *Science* | 60 out of | 80 |
| *Maths* | 75 out of | 100 |
| *English* | 38 out of | 50 |
| *French* | 28 out of | 40 |

   (a)    Express his score for each test as a percentage.

   (b)    Write down his average percentage score for the 4 tests.

# 9.4  Finding Percentages

In this section we revise finding percentages of quantities.

## Example 1

Calculate 20% of £120.

## Solution

$$20\% \text{ of } £120 = \frac{20}{100} \times 120$$

$$= \frac{2}{10} \times 120$$

$$= £24$$

## Example 2

Calculate 75% of 48 kg.

## Solution

$$75\% \text{ of } 48 \text{ kg} = \frac{75}{100} \times 48$$

$$= \frac{3}{4} \times 48$$

$$= 36 \text{ kg}$$

Value Added Tax (VAT) is added to the price of many products; in the UK it is currently $17\frac{1}{2}\%$. An interesting way to calculate $17\frac{1}{2}\%$ is to use the fact that $17\frac{1}{2} = 10 + 5 + 2\frac{1}{2}$; this is illustrated in the next example.

## Example 3

A bike costs £180 before VAT is added. How much VAT must be added to the cost of the bike, if VAT is charged at $17\frac{1}{2}\%$ ?

## Solution

$$10\% \quad \text{of } £180 = £18$$

$$5\% \quad \text{of } £180 = £9$$

$$2\frac{1}{2}\% \quad \text{of } £180 = £4.50$$

$$17\frac{1}{2}\% \quad \text{of } £180 = £18 + £9 + £4.50$$

$$= £31.50$$

## Exercises

1. Calculate:

   (a) 50% of £22     (b) 10% of 70 m     (c) 25% of £60

   (d) 30% of 80 m     (e) 60% of £40     (f) 90% of 50 kg

   (g) 75% of £30     (h) 25% of 6 kg     (i) 30% of 32 kg

   (j) 16% of £40     (k) 70% of 8 m     (l) 35% of £20

2. Use the method of Example 3 to calculate the VAT that must be added to the following prices at a rate of $17\frac{1}{2}$%:

   (a) £200     (b) £300     (c) £40

   (d) £30     (e) £28     (f) £38

3. (a) Calculate $17\frac{1}{2}$% of £25

   (b) Describe the most sensible way to give your answer.

4. Calculate $17\frac{1}{2}$% of the following amounts, giving your answers to a sensible degree of accuracy:

   (a) £15     (b) £75     (c) £7

5. Use a method similar to Example 3 to calculate 15% of £120.

6. A computer costs £900, but $17\frac{1}{2}$% VAT must be added to this price.

   (a) Calculate $17\frac{1}{2}$% of £900.

   (b) Calculate the total cost of the computer.

7. A company employs 240 staff. The number of staff is to be increased by 20%. How many *new* staff will the company employ?

8. A bike costs £186. The price is to be reduced by $33\frac{1}{3}$% in a sale.

   (a) Calculate how much you would save by buying the bike in the sale.

   (b) How much would you pay for the bike in the sale?

9. In a school there are 280 pupils in Year 7. 85% of these pupils go on a trip to Alton Towers. How many pupils go on the trip?

10. Alec scores 75% on a test with a maximum of 56 marks. How many marks does Alec score in the test?

# 9.5 Increasing and Decreasing Quantities by a Percentage

When increasing or decreasing by a percentage there are two possible approaches: one is to find the actual increase or decrease and to add it to, or subtract it from, the original amount. The second approach is to use a simple multiplication. For example, to increase by 20%, multiply by 1.2. We can illustrate this by considering a price, say £$p$, that increases by 20%.

The increase is $£p \times \dfrac{20}{100} = £0.2\,p$

so the new price is

$$£p + £0.2p = £(1 + 0.2)p$$

$$= £1.2p$$

and we can see that a 20% increase is equivalent to multiplying by 1.2 to get the new price.

Note that

$$100\% + 20\% = 120\% \Rightarrow \dfrac{120}{100} = 1.2$$

Similarly, a decrease of 20% is equivalent to

$$100\% - 20\% = 80\% \Rightarrow \dfrac{80}{100} = 0.8$$

i.e. a multiplication by 0.8.

## Example 1

The price of a jar of coffee is £2.00. Calculate the new price after an increase of 10%.

## Solution

$10\%$ of £2.00 $= \dfrac{10}{100} \times 2$ \qquad or \qquad $100\% + 10\% = 110\%,$

$= £0.2$ \qquad\qquad\qquad so multiply by 1.1

New price $= 2 + 0.2$ \qquad\qquad\qquad New price $= 1.1 \times £2$

$= £2.20$ \qquad\qquad\qquad\qquad $= £2.20$

## Example 2

In a sale, the price of a TV is reduced by 40%. What is the sale price if the original price was £170.

## Solution

$$40\% \text{ of } £170 \quad = \quad \frac{40}{100} \times 170 \qquad \text{or} \qquad 100\% - 40\% \ = \ 60\%,$$

$$= \ £68 \qquad\qquad\qquad\qquad \text{so multiply by } 0.6$$

$$\text{Sale price} \ = \ 170 - 68 \qquad\qquad\qquad \text{Sale price} \ = \ 0.6 \times 170$$

$$= \ £102 \qquad\qquad\qquad\qquad\qquad\qquad = \ £102$$

## Example 3

Jared earns £24 each week by working in a shop. His wages are to be increased by 5%. How much will he then earn each week?

## Solution

$$5\% \text{ of } £24 \ = \ \frac{5}{100} \times 24 \qquad\qquad \text{or} \qquad 100\% + 5\% \ = \ 105\%,$$

$$= \ £1.20 \qquad\qquad\qquad\qquad \text{so multiply by } 1.05$$

$$\text{New wages} \ = \ 24 + 1.20 \qquad\qquad\qquad \text{New wages} \ = \ 1.05 \times 24$$

$$= \ £25.20 \qquad\qquad\qquad\qquad\qquad\qquad = \ £25.20$$

## Exercises

1.  Add 10% to:

    (a)  £40              (b)  £136              (c)  £262

2.  Reduce the following prices by 20%:

    (a)  £50              (b)  £92              (c)  £340

3.  (a)  Increase 40 m by 30%          (b)  Increase £60 by 5%

    (c)  Increase £66 by 20%          (d)  Increase 80 kg by 40%

    (e)  Increase £1000 by 30%        (f)  Decrease £60 by 25%

    (g)  Reduce 70 kg by 5%          (h)  Reduce £90 by 15%

    (i)  Increase 40 m by 7%          (j)  Increase £18 by 4%

4.  A computer costs £600.  In a sale there is a 20% discount on the price of the item.  Calculate the sale price of the computer.

5.  A shopkeeper increases all the prices in his shop by 4%.  What is the new price of each of the items below?  Give your answers to the nearest penny.

    | | |
    |---|---|
    | *Box of chocolates* | £3 |
    | *Bag of flour* | 75p |
    | *Packet of sweets* | 50p |
    | *Tin of beans* | 20p |
    | *Can of drink* | 45p |

6.  A CD player costs £90.  In a sale the price is reduced by 25%.  Calculate the sale price.

7.  A certain type of calculator costs £8.  A teacher buys 30 of these calculators for her school and is given a 20% discount.  How much does she pay in total?

8.  Add $17\frac{1}{2}$% VAT to the following prices, giving your answers to the nearest pence:

    (a)  £400          (b)  £22          (c)  £65

9.  The population of a town is 120 000.  What is the total population of the town after a 5% increase?

10. Hannah invests £800 in a building society.  Every year 5% interest is added to her money.

    (a)  Explain why, after 2 years she has £882 in her account.

    (b)  How much money does she have after 5 years?  (Give your answer to the nearest pence.)

11. Andrew has £100 to invest in a building society.  At the end of each year, 10% interest is added to his investment.

    (a)  What is the multiplier that can be used each year to calculate the new amount in the account?

    (b)  Show that the multiplier for 2 years is 1.21.

    (c)  What is the multiplier for $n$ years?

    (d)  How many years does it take to *double* the £100 investment?

# 9.6 Finding the Percentage Increase and Decrease

When a quantity increases, we can find the percentage increase using this formula:

$$\text{Percentage } increase = \frac{\text{increase}}{\text{original amount}} \times 100$$

Similarly,

$$\text{Percentage } decrease = \frac{\text{decrease}}{\text{original amount}} \times 100$$

### Example 1

The price of a drink increases from 40p to 45p. What is the percentage increase?

**Solution**

Increase = 45p − 40p

= 5p

Percentage increase = $\dfrac{5}{40} \times 100$

= $\dfrac{25}{2}$

= 12.5%

### Example 2

The number of pupils in a school increases from 820 to 861. Calculate the percentage increase.

**Solution**

Increase = 861 − 820

= 41 pupils

Percentage increase = $\dfrac{41}{820} \times 100$

= 5%

## Example 3

Although the lion is thought of as an African animal, there is a small population in India and elsewhere in Asia. The number of lions in India decreased from 6000 to 3900 over a 10-year period. Calculate the percentage decrease in this period.

## Solution

Decrease $=$ 6000 − 3900

$\qquad = $ 2100 lions

Percentage decrease $= \dfrac{2100}{6000} \times 100$

$\qquad\qquad\qquad = $ 35%

## Example 4

The price of cheese, per kg, is increased from £3.26 to £3.84. What is the percentage increase?

## Solution

Increase $=$ £3.84 − £3.26

$\qquad = $ £0.58

Percentage increase $= \dfrac{0.58}{3.26} \times 100$

$\qquad\qquad\qquad = $ 17.8% to 1 decimal place

Note: You might find it easier to work through the example in pence, but note that *all* quantities must be expressed in pence.

$\qquad$ Increase $= \left(384 - 326\right) \text{p}$

$\qquad\qquad\quad = $ 58p

$\qquad$ Percentage increase $= \dfrac{58}{326} \times 100$

$\qquad\qquad\qquad\qquad = $ 17.8% to 1 decimal place

## Example 5

In a sale, the price of a bike is reduced from £180 to £138. Calculate the percentage reduction in price, correct to 1 decimal place.

## Solution

Reduction $= 180 - 138$

$\qquad = £42$

Percentage reduction $= \dfrac{42}{180} \times 100$

$\qquad\qquad\qquad = 23.3\%$ to 1 decimal place.

## Exercises

1.  The price of a school lunch increases from £1.40 to £1.54. Calculate the percentage increase in the price.

2.  A television priced at £500 is reduced in price to £400 in a sale. Calculate the percentage reduction in the price of the television.

3.  The price of a car increases from £8000 to £8240. What is the percentage increase in the price of the car?

4.  A shopkeeper buys notepads for 60p each and sells them for 80p each. What percentage of the selling price is profit?

5.  The value of an antique clock increases from £300 to £345. Calculate the percentage increase in the value of the clock.

6.  The number of books in a school library is increased from 2220 to 2354. What is the percentage increase in the number of books?

7.  The height of a tomato plant increases from 80 cm to 95 cm. Calculate the percentage increase in the height, correct to 1 decimal place.

8.  The price of a bus fare is reduced from 55p to 40p. Calculate the percentage reduction in the price of the bus fare, correct to 1 decimal place.

9.  The mass of a person on a diet decreases from 75 kg to 74 kg. Calculate the percentage reduction in their mass, correct to 3 significant figures.

10. Jasmine invests £250 in a building society. After the first year her account contains £262.50. After the second year it contains £280.88. Calculate the percentage increase of the amount in her account:

    (a) during the first year,

    (b) during the second year,

    (c) over the two years.

    Give your answers correct to 2 decimal places.

# 9.7 Reverse Percentage Calculations

The process of adding a percentage to a quantity can be reversed.

For example, if the cost of a portable TV is £141 including $17\frac{1}{2}$% VAT, the cost *before* adding the VAT can be found. The multiplier in this example is 1.175, as the price is made up of $100\% + 17.5\% = 117.5\%$, which is equivalent to multiplying by

$$\frac{117.5}{100} = 1.175$$

| Original price | $\xrightarrow{\times 1.175}$ | £141 |
|---|---|---|
| £120 | $\xleftarrow{\div 1.175}$ | £141 |

## Example 1

Jane's salary was increased by 10% to £9350. What was her original salary?

## Solution

$100\% + 10\% = 110\%$,

which $= \dfrac{110}{100} = 1.1$

Therefore Jane's original salary would have been multiplied by 1.1 to give £9350.

So to calculate her original salary, divide by 1.1.

| Original salary | $\xrightarrow{\times 1.1}$ | £9350 |
|---|---|---|
| £8500 | $\xleftarrow{\div 1.1}$ | £9350 |

## Example 2

In a sale, the price of a video recorder is reduced by 22% to £218.40. How much money would you save by buying the video recorder in the sale?

### Solution

$100\% - 22\% = 78\%$

$$= \frac{78}{100}$$

$$= 0.78$$

The original price would have been multiplied by 0.78 to get the sale price. So divide by 0.78 to find the original price.

Original price $\xrightarrow{\times 0.78}$ £218.40

£280 $\xleftarrow{\div 0.78}$ £218.40

Saving = Original price − Sale price

= £280 − £218.40

= £61.60

## Example 3

The cost of an order, including VAT at $17\frac{1}{2}\%$, is £274.95.

Calculate the cost of the order *without* VAT.

### Solution

Original cost $\xrightarrow{\times 1.175}$ £274.95

£234 $\xleftarrow{\div 1.175}$ £274.95

Cost of the order without VAT is £234.00.

# Exercises

1. In a sale the prices of all the clothes in a shop are reduced by 20%. Calculate the original prices of the items below:

| Item | Sale Price |
|---|---|
| Jeans | £36 |
| Coat | £56 |
| Shirt | £14 |

2. The price of a car is increased by 4% to £12 480. What was the original price?

3. The amount that Jason earns for his paper round is increased by 2% to £21.93 per week. How much *extra* money does Jason now get each week?

4. A special value packet of breakfast cereal contains 25% more than the standard packet. The special value packet contains 562.5 grams of cereal. How much does the *standard* packet contain?

5. The bill for repairing a computer is £29.38 which includes VAT at $17\frac{1}{2}$%. What was the bill before the VAT was added?

6. The height of a plant increases by 18%, to 26 cm. Calculate the original height of the plant, correct to the nearest cm.

7. A 3.5% pay rise increases Mr Smith's annual salary to £21 735. What was his original salary?

8. The price of a bike in a sale is £145. If the original price has been reduced by $12\frac{1}{2}$%, what was the original price? (Give your answer to the nearest pence.)

9. Alice carries out an experiment to record how quickly plants grow. One plant increases in height from 12.0 cm to 13.8 cm in one week. A second plant increases by the same percentage to 16.1 cm. What was the original height of the second plant?

10. James buys a computer. The seller reduces the price by 30% and adds VAT at 17.5%. If James pays £1551 for the computer, what was its original price? (Give your answer to the nearest pence.)

# 10 Probability - Two Events

## 10.1 Recap: Basic Probability for One Event

In this section we revise the use of probabilities for single events, remembering that:

$$\text{Probability of an event} = \frac{\text{number of } \textit{successful} \text{ outcomes}}{\text{number of } \textit{possible} \text{ outcomes}}$$

### Example 1

A tube of sweets contains 10 red sweets, 7 blue sweets, 8 green sweets and 5 orange sweets. If a sweet is taken at random from the tube, what is the probability that it is:

(a)   red,

(b)   orange,

(c)   green *or* red,

(d)   *not* blue ?

### Solution

There are 30 sweets in the tube.

(a)   There are 10 red sweets in the tube, so

$$p\,(\text{red}) = \frac{10}{30}$$

$$= \frac{1}{3}$$

(b)   There are 5 orange sweets in the tube, so

$$p\,(\text{orange}) = \frac{5}{30}$$

$$= \frac{1}{6}$$

(c)    There are 8 green sweets and 10 red sweets in the tube, so

$$p \text{ (green or red)} \ = \ \frac{8 + 10}{30}$$

$$= \ \frac{18}{30}$$

$$= \ \frac{3}{5}$$

(d)    There are 23 sweets that are *not* blue in the tube, so

$$p \text{ (not blue)} \ = \ \frac{23}{30}$$

## Example 2

Nine balls, each marked with a number from 1 to 9, are placed in a bag and one ball is taken out at random. What is the probability that the number on the ball is:

(a)    odd,

(b)    a multiple of 3,

(c)    a 5,

(d)    not a 7 ?

## Solution

There are 9 possible outcomes in each case.

(a)    There are 5 possible odd numbers, so

$$p \text{ (odd)} \ = \ \frac{5}{9}$$

(b)    There are 3 numbers that are multiples of 3, so

$$p \text{ (multiple of 3)} \ = \ \frac{3}{9}$$

$$= \ \frac{1}{3}$$

(c)    There is only 1 ball numbered 5, so

$$p \text{ (5)} \ = \ \frac{1}{9}$$

(d)    There are 8 numbers that are *not* 7, so

$$p \text{ (not 7)} \ = \ \frac{8}{9}$$

## Exercises

1. There are 16 girls and 8 boys in the tennis club. One of these is chosen at random to enter a competition. What is the probability that a girl is chosen?

2. A bag contains 8 blue balls, 7 green balls and 5 red balls. A ball is taken at random from the bag. What is the probability that the ball is:

   (a) red,

   (b) blue,

   (c) green,

   (d) yellow?

3. A card is taken at random from a standard 52-card pack of playing cards. What is the probability that it is:

   (a) a seven,

   (b) a heart,

   (c) a red card,

   (d) a red six ?

4. If you roll a fair dice, what is the probability that the number you get is:

   (a) 5

   (b) an odd number,

   (c) a number greater than 1,

   (d) a multiple of 4 ?

5. Ishmail writes a computer program that produces at random one of the digits

   0, 1, 2, 3, 4, 5, 6, 7, 8, 9.

   What is the probability that the program produces:

   (a) an even number,

   (b) a multiple of 4,

   (c) a number less than 7,

   (d) a multiple of 5 ?

6. The police line up 10 people in an identity parade; only one of the people is the criminal. A witness does not recognise the criminal and so chooses a person at random. What is the probability that:

   (a) the criminal is chosen,

   (b) the criminal is *not* chosen ?

7.  There are 18 boys and 17 girls in a class. One of these pupils is selected at random to represent the class. What is the probability that the pupil selected is a girl?

8.  In Hannah's purse there are three £1 coins, five 10p coins and eight 2p coins. If she takes a coin at random from her purse, what is the probability that it is:

    (a)  a £1 coin,

    (b)  a 2p coin,

    (c)  *not* a £1 coin,

    (d)  a £1 coin *or* a 10p coin ?

9.  Some of the children in a class write down the first letter of their surname on a card; these cards are shown below:

    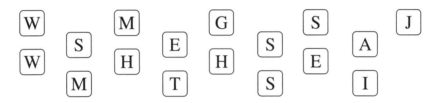

    (a)  One of these cards is taken at random. What is the probability that the letter on it is:

        (i)    W,

        (ii)   S *or* T,

        (iii)  J *or* M,

        (iv)   *not* H

        (v)    a vowel ?

    (b)  Which letter is the most likely to be chosen?

10. Rachel buys a new CD, on which is her favourite track, 8 other tracks she likes and 2 tracks that she does not like. She sets her CD player to play at random. What is the probability that the first track it plays is:

    (a)  Rachel's favourite,

    (b)  a track that she likes,

    (c)  a track that she does *not* like ?

# 10.2 Outcomes with Two Events

When two events take place at the same time, it is important to list *all* the possible outcomes in some way. There are three possible approaches: *systematic listing, using a table* or *using a tree diagram.*

## Example 1

Caitlin and Dave each buy a chocolate bar from a vending machine that sells *Aero, Bounty, Crunchie* and *Dime* bars.

List the possible pairs of bars which Caitlin and Dave can choose.

## Solution

| Caitlin | Dave |
|---------|------|
| A | A |
| A | B |
| A | C |
| A | D |
| B | A |
| B | B |
| B | C |
| B | D |
| C | A |
| C | B |
| C | C |
| C | D |
| D | A |
| D | B |
| D | C |
| D | D |

A  =  *Aero*

B  =  *Bounty*

C  =  *Crunchie*

D  =  *Dime*

## Example 2

A fair dice is rolled and an unbiased coin is tossed. Draw a table to show the possible outcomes.

### Solution

*Possibilities for coin*

*Possibilities for dice*

|  |  | DICE | | | | | |
|---|---|---|---|---|---|---|---|
|  |  | *1* | *2* | *3* | *4* | *5* | *6* |
| COIN | H | H1 | H2 | H3 | H4 | H5 | H6 |
|  | T | T1 | T2 | T3 | T4 | T5 | T6 |

The table shows that there are 12 possible outcomes.

## Example 3

Draw a table to show all the possible total scores when two fair dice are thrown at the same time.

### Solution

|  |  | DICE B | | | | | |
|---|---|---|---|---|---|---|---|
|  |  | *1* | *2* | *3* | *4* | *5* | *6* |
| D I C E A | *1* | 2 | 3 | 4 | 5 | 6 | 7 |
|  | *2* | 3 | 4 | 5 | 6 | 7 | 8 |
|  | *3* | 4 | 5 | 6 | 7 | 8 | 9 |
|  | *4* | 5 | 6 | 7 | 8 | 9 | 10 |
|  | *5* | 6 | 7 | 8 | 9 | 10 | 11 |
|  | *6* | 7 | 8 | 9 | 10 | 11 | 12 |

The table shows that there are 36 possible outcomes, and gives the total score for each outcome.

From the table it can be seen that there are 6 outcomes that give a score of 7.

## Example 4

Use a tree diagram to show the possible outcomes when two unbiased coins are tossed.

### Solution

The diagram shows that there are 4 possible outcomes.

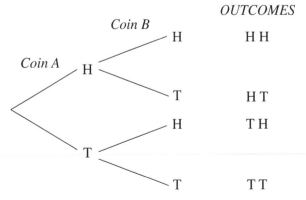

MEP Y8 Practice Book A

## Example 5

In a drawer there are some white socks and some black socks. Tim takes out one sock and then a second. Draw a tree diagram to show the possible outcomes.

**Solution**

There are four possible outcomes, of which two will will produce two socks of the same colour.

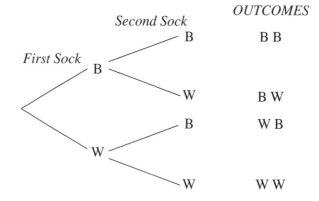

*OUTCOMES*

*Second Sock*

*First Sock*

B — B    B B

B — W    B W

W — B    W B

W — W    W W

## Exercises

1. Copy and complete the table to show all possible outcomes when 2 fair coins are tossed.

|  |  | COIN B | |
|---|---|---|---|
|  |  | H | T |
| COIN A | H |  |  |
|  | T |  |  |

2. Two spinners are numbered 1 to 4 as shown in the diagram:

   (a) Copy and complete the table below, to show all possible outcomes when they are spun, writing the *total score* for each outcome.

 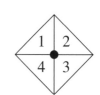

|  |  | SPINNER B | | | |
|---|---|---|---|---|---|
|  |  | 1 | 2 | 3 | 4 |
| SPINNER A | 1 |  |  |  |  |
|  | 2 |  |  |  |  |
|  | 3 |  |  |  |  |
|  | 4 |  |  |  |  |

   (b) What is the total number of possible outcomes?

   (c) How many outcomes give a score of 5 ?

3.  Two fair dice are renumbered using  −2, −1, 0, 1, 2, 3  instead of the usual numbers.  The two dice are thrown in the normal way.

    (a)  Draw a table to show the total score for each of the possible outcomes.

    (b)  How many ways are there of scoring 0 ?

4.  The two spinners shown in the diagram opposite, are spun at the same time:

    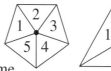

    (a)  Draw a table to show all possible outcomes, and the total score for each outcome.

    (b)  How many different outcomes are there?

    (c)  How many outcomes give a score of 6 ?

5.  In a bag there are red and blue counters.  Two counters are taken out of the bag at random.

    (a)  Copy and complete the tree diagram below, to show all outcomes:

    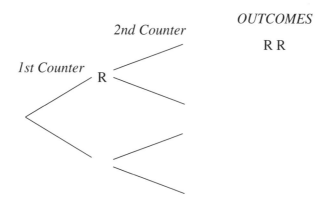

    (b)  How many outcomes include a *red* counter?

    (c)  How many outcomes include a *blue* counter?

6.  (a)  Draw a tree diagram to show all possible outcomes when two unbiased coins are tossed.

    (b)  Extend your tree diagram to show the possible outcomes when three unbiased coins are tossed.

    (c)  How many outcomes are there when three unbiased coins are tossed?

    (d)  How many outcomes are there when four unbiased coins are tossed?

7.  In a jar there are three different types of sweets, *eclairs, mints* and *toffees*; two sweets are taken at random.

    (a)  Draw a tree diagram to show the possible outcomes.

    (b)  How many of the outcomes include a *toffee*?

    (c)  How many of the outcomes include a *mint* and a *toffee*?

8.    A red dice, a blue dice and a green dice are put into a bag; all the dice are fair. One is then taken out and rolled. The colour of the dice and the score shown are recorded.

      (a)    How many possible outcomes are there?

      (b)    How many outcomes include a 5 ?

9.    In a game, two fair dice are rolled and the scores are multiplied together.

      (a)    Draw a table to show the possible outcomes and their scores.

      (b)    How many ways are there of scoring 12 ?

      (c)    How many ways are there of scoring 18 ?

10.   A bag contains a mixture of red, green and white balls. Three balls are taken at random from the bag.

      (a)    Write down all possible outcomes.

      (b)    How many outcomes include a red ball?

      (c)    How many outcomes include a red or a white ball?

      (d)    How many outcomes include a red and a green ball?

# 10.3 Probability Using Listings

When the outcomes for two events are equally likely, the probabilities of particular outcomes can be found.

## Example 1

Look at the list of chocolate bars which can be chosen by Caitlin and Dave in Example 1 of section 10.2. What is the probability that they both choose the *same* type of chocolate bar?

## Solution

There are 16 different outcomes and all are equally likely.

In 4 of these outcomes both Caitlin and Dave choose the same type of bar.

So

$$p\,(\text{same type}) \;=\; \frac{4}{16} \quad \text{or} \quad \frac{1}{4}$$

## Example 2

When two unbiased coins are tossed, determine the probability of obtaining:

(a)     two heads,

(b)     two tails,

(c)     a head and a tail.

## Solution

The table shows the possible outcomes:

In this situation there are 4 outcomes that are equally likely.

|   | H | T |
|---|---|---|
| H | H H | H H |
| T | T H | T H |

(a)     Here 1 of the 4 outcomes gives 2 heads, so

$$p\,(2\text{ heads})\ =\ \frac{1}{4}$$

(b)     Here 1 of the 4 outcomes gives 2 tails, so

$$p\,(2\text{ tails})\ =\ \frac{1}{4}$$

(c)     Here 2 of the outcomes gives a head and a tail, so

$$p\,(\text{head and a tail})\ =\ \frac{2}{4}$$
$$=\ \frac{1}{2}$$

## Example 3

Two fair dice are rolled at the same time.  What is the probability that the total score is:

(a)     6,

(b)     greater than 9,

(c)     less than 7 ?

## Solution

The table show the possible outcomes.

There are 36 equally likely scores.

(a)     There are 5 outcomes that give a score of 6, so

$$p\,(6)\ =\ \frac{5}{36}$$

|   | 1 | 2 | 3 | 4 | 5 | 6 |
|---|---|---|---|---|---|---|
| 1 | 2 | 3 | 4 | 5 | 6 | 7 |
| 2 | 3 | 4 | 5 | 6 | 7 | 8 |
| 3 | 4 | 5 | 6 | 7 | 8 | 9 |
| 4 | 5 | 6 | 7 | 8 | 9 | 10 |
| 5 | 6 | 7 | 8 | 9 | 10 | 11 |
| 6 | 7 | 8 | 9 | 10 | 11 | 12 |

(b)    There are 6 outcomes that give a score greater than 9, so

$$p \text{ (greater than 9)} = \frac{6}{36}$$

$$= \frac{1}{6}$$

(c)    There are 15 outcomes that give scores of less than 7, so

$$p \text{ (less than 7)} = \frac{15}{36}$$

$$= \frac{5}{12}$$

## Exercises

1.    Use information from the table in Example 3 to answer this question:

When two fair dice are thrown, what is the probability that the total score is:

(a)    9,                                    (b)    an odd number,

(c)    greater than 10,                      (d)    less than 8 ?

2.    The diagram shows two spinners which are both spun.
      What is the probability that the total score on the two spinners is:

(a)    7,                    (b)    6,

(c)    greater than 10,     (d)    less than 5 ?

3.    An unbiased coin is tossed and a fair dice is thrown.  Use a table of outcomes to determine the probability of each of the following:

(a)    obtaining a head and a 3,

(b)    obtaining a tail and an even number,

(c)    obtaining a head and a prime number.

4.    The two spinners shown in the diagram are both spun.

(a)    Draw up a table to show the possible outcomes.

(b)    What is the probability that both spinners show the same colour?

(c)    What is the probability of obtaining a yellow and a red?

(d)    What is the probability of obtaining a red and a blue?

5.    The diagram shows two spinners that are spun at the same time:

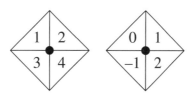

Use a table to determine the probability of obtaining a total score of:

(a)   6              (b)   0                  (c)   1                  (d)   3

6.    For the spinners in question 5, determine the probability of obtaining a total score that is:

(a)   an even number,

(b)   greater than 1,

(c)   less than 1,

(d)   less than 6.

7.    Two unbiased coins are tossed at the same time.  What is the probability of obtaining:

(a)   at least one head,

(b)   no heads ?

8.    Three unbiased coins are tossed at the same time.  Use a tree diagram to show the outcomes and determine the probability of obtaining:

(a)   3 heads,

(b)   at least 1 head,

(c)   at least 2 heads.

9.    Two fair dice are rolled and the scores on each dice are multiplied together to give a total score.  What is the probability of getting a total score:

(a)   of 12,

(b)   of 20,

(c)   greater than 25,

(d)   less than 30,

(e)   that is an even number ?

10.   If 4 unbiased coins are tossed at the same time, what is the probability of obtaining the same number of heads as tails?

# 10.4 Multiplication Law for Independent Events

Probabilities can be assigned to tree diagrams, and then multiplication can be used to determine the probabilities for combined events.

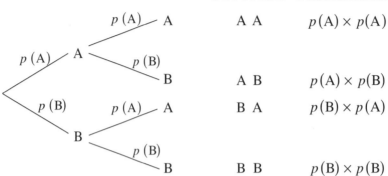

|  | *OUTCOMES* | *PROBABILITIES* |
|---|---|---|
|  | A A | $p(A) \times p(A)$ |
|  | A B | $p(A) \times p(B)$ |
|  | B A | $p(B) \times p(A)$ |
|  | B B | $p(B) \times p(B)$ |

Note:   Here we have an experiment with two possible outcomes, A and B, and the experiment is repeated once.  It is assumed that the probability of either A or B remains the *same* when the experiment is repeated; in this case, we say that A and B are *independent* events.

## Example 1

Two fair dice are rolled.  Use a tree diagram to determine the probability of obtaining:

(a)   2 sixes,          (b)   1 six,          (c)   no sixes.

## Solution

The tree diagram is shown below:

| | *OUTCOMES* | *PROBABILITIES* |
|---|---|---|
| | 6, 6 | $\frac{1}{6} \times \frac{1}{6} = \frac{1}{36}$ |
| | 6, NOT 6 | $\frac{1}{6} \times \frac{5}{6} = \frac{5}{36}$ |
| | NOT 6, 6 | $\frac{5}{6} \times \frac{1}{6} = \frac{5}{36}$ |
| | NOT 6, NOT 6 | $\frac{5}{6} \times \frac{5}{6} = \frac{25}{36}$ |

$$\text{total} = \frac{36}{36} = 1$$

(a)   $p(2 \text{ sixes}) = \dfrac{1}{36}$

(b)   $p(1 \text{ six}) = \dfrac{5}{36} + \dfrac{5}{36} = \dfrac{10}{36} = \dfrac{5}{18}$

(c)   $p(\text{no sixes}) = \dfrac{25}{36}$

*Note that these probabilities add up to 1. This will always be so when the probabilities are added from the outcome of the tree diagram. This is a very useful means of checking your working.*

## Example 2

A bag contains 4 red balls and 3 green balls. A ball is taken out at random, and then put back; a second ball is then taken from the bag. What is the probability that:

(a)   both balls are the same colour,

(b)   at least one of the balls is green,

(c)   the balls are of different colours?

## Solution

Use a tree diagram:

| 2nd Ball | OUTCOMES | PROBABILITIES |

1st Ball

$\frac{4}{7}$   R

$\frac{4}{7}$ — R   R R   $\frac{4}{7} \times \frac{4}{7} = \frac{16}{49}$

$\frac{3}{7}$ — G   R G   $\frac{4}{7} \times \frac{3}{7} = \frac{12}{49}$

$\frac{3}{7}$   G

$\frac{4}{7}$ — R   G R   $\frac{3}{7} \times \frac{4}{7} = \frac{12}{49}$

$\frac{3}{7}$ — G   G G   $\frac{3}{7} \times \frac{3}{7} = \frac{9}{49}$

total $= \frac{49}{49} = 1$

(a)   $p(\text{both the same}) = p(R R \text{ or } G G)$

$= p(R R) + p(G G)$

$= \frac{16}{49} + \frac{9}{49}$

$= \frac{25}{49}$

(b)   $p(\text{at least one green ball})$

$= p(G G \text{ or } G R \text{ or } R G)$     or     $= 1 - p(R R)$

$= p(G G) + p(G R) + p(R G)$          $= 1 - \frac{16}{49}$

$= \frac{9}{49} + \frac{12}{49} + \frac{12}{49}$          $= \frac{33}{49}$

$= \frac{33}{49}$

(c)    $p(\text{both different colours}) = p(\text{R G or G R})$

$$= p(\text{R G}) + p(\text{G R})$$

$$= \frac{12}{49} + \frac{12}{49}$$

$$= \frac{24}{49}$$

Note: In probability questions of this type, 'or' means adding the probabilities.

## Example 3

On her way to work, Sylvia drives through three sets of traffic lights. The probability of each set of lights being green is 0.3. What is the probability that they are *all* green?

## Solution

$p(\text{all green}) = p(\text{1st green and 2nd green and 3rd green})$

$$= p(\text{1st green}) \times p(\text{2nd green}) \times p(\text{3rd green})$$

$$= 0.3 \times 0.3 \times 0.3 \quad [\text{or } 0.3^3]$$

$$= 0.027$$

Note: In probability questions of this type, 'and' means multiplying the probabilities.

*Remember*    A tree diagram is drawn when it will *help* you to analyse a problem; so if it will help, draw one. On the other hand, if you are able to solve a problem *without* one (see Example 3 above), then do so.

## Example 4

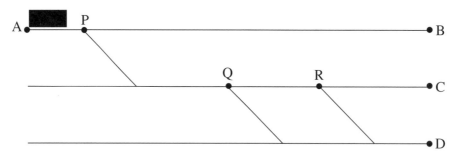

The diagram shows a model railway track. At each of the junctions P, Q and R, the probability of a train going straight ahead is $\frac{2}{3}$ and the probability of it branching to the right is $\frac{1}{3}$.

A train starts at point A.

(a)    What is the probability that it reaches point C?

(b)    What is the probability that it reaches point D ?

## Solution

(a)    $p(\text{right and straight and straight})$ $= \dfrac{1}{3} \times \dfrac{2}{3} \times \dfrac{2}{3}$

$= \dfrac{4}{27}$

(b)    $p\big((\text{right and right}) \text{ or } (\text{right and straight and right})\big)$

$= \dfrac{1}{3} \times \dfrac{1}{3} + \dfrac{1}{3} \times \dfrac{2}{3} \times \dfrac{1}{3}$

$= \dfrac{1}{9} + \dfrac{2}{27}$

$= \dfrac{5}{27}$

## Exercises

1.    A bag contains 3 red balls and 2 blue balls. A ball is taken at random from the bag and then put back. A second ball is then taken out of the bag.
       What is the probability that:
       (a)    both balls are red,

       (b)    both balls are the same colour,

       (c)    at least one of the balls is red ?

2.    Repeat question 1 for a bag with 7 red balls and 3 blue balls.

3.    Two fair dice are rolled at the same time. Use a tree diagram to determine the probability of obtaining:
       (a)    two even numbers,

       (b)    at least one even number,

       (c)    no even numbers.

4.    Two fair dice are rolled at the same time. Use a tree diagram to determine the probability of obtaining:
       (a)    two multiples of 3,

       (b)    exactly one multiple of 3,

       (c)    less than two multiples of 3.

5.    A coin has been weighted, so that the probability of getting a head is $\frac{2}{5}$ and

      the probability of getting a tail is $\frac{3}{5}$; the coin is thrown twice.  Determine
      the probability of obtaining:

      (a)    2 heads,              (b)    no heads,              (c)    at least one head.

6.    The spinner shown in the diagram is spun twice.
      Use a tree diagram to determine the probability
      of obtaining:

      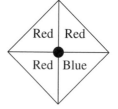

      (a)    2 reds,              (b)    at least one red,

      (c)    no reds.

7.    The spinner in the diagram is spun twice.  Determine
      the probability of obtaining:

      (a)    at least one A,      (b)    at least one B,

      (c)    two As,              (d)    two Bs.

8.    The spinner in question 6 is spun 3 times.  Use a tree diagram to determine
      the probability of obtaining:

      (a)    3 reds,              (b)    2 reds,              (c)    at least 1 red.

9.    A bag contains 1 red ball, 2 green balls and 4 yellow balls.  A ball is taken
      from the bag at random.  The ball is then put back, and a second ball is
      taken at random from the bag.

      What is the probability that:

      (a)    both balls are the same colour,

      (b)    no yellow balls are taken out,

      (c)    at least one yellow ball is taken out?

10.   Each of 10 balls is marked with a different number from 1 to 10.  One ball
      is taken at random and then replaced.  A second ball is then taken at
      random.  Determine the probability that:

      (a)    both balls taken are marked with the number 5,

      (b)    both balls taken have even numbers,

      (c)    both balls taken have numbers which are multiples of 3,

      (d)    at least one of the balls taken has a number greater than 2.

11.   On his way to work, Paul has to pass through 2 sets of traffic lights.  The
      probability that the first set of lights is green is 0.5, and the probability that
      the second set of lights is green is 0.4.

      What is the probability that *both* sets of lights are green?

12. On her way to the theatre, Sheila passes through 3 sets of traffic lights. The probability that each set of lights is green is $\frac{1}{3}$.

    (a) What is the probability that *none* of the lights is green?

    (b) What is the probability that *two sets* of lights are green and the other set is not green?

13.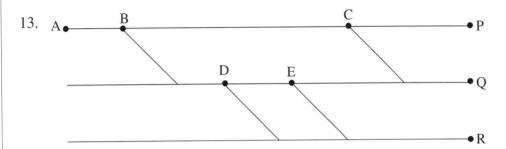

    The diagram shows a section of a railway track. At each of the junctions B, C, D and E, the probability of going straight on is $\frac{3}{4}$.
    The train starts at A.

    (a) What is the probability that it reaches P?

    (b) What is the probability that it reaches Q?

14.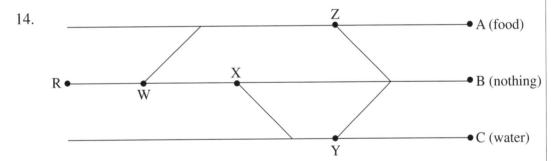

    A rat leaves position R and starts walking towards B. If it reaches B it gets nothing, if it reaches A it gets food and if it reaches C it gets water.

    At each of the junctions W, X, Y and Z, the probability of going straight on is 0.6 and the probability of branching off is 0.4.

    (a) What is the probability that the rat gets *food*?

    (b) What is the probability that the rat gets *water*?

    (c) What is the probability that it gets *nothing*?

15. When two fair dice are thrown, what is the probability that the score on the second dice is higher than the score on the first dice?

# 10.5 Conditional Probability

In some situations where events are repeated, the probabilities will change after the first event. For example, consider a bag containing 8 red balls and 3 blue balls.

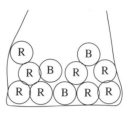

The probability that a ball taken at random is red is $\dfrac{8}{11}$.

If a second ball is taken out *without the first ball being replaced*, then:

EITHER   the first ball was *red*, so the probability that the second ball is red is

$\dfrac{7}{10}$, since there are 3 blue balls but only 7 red balls left.

OR         the first ball was *blue*, so the probability that the second is red is

$\dfrac{8}{10} = \dfrac{4}{5}$, since there are 8 red balls but only 2 blue balls left.

Tree diagrams are very useful for this type of problems.

## Example 1

A bag contains 7 yellow balls and 5 red balls. One ball is taken from the bag at random, and is not replaced. A second ball is then taken from the bag.
Determine the probability that:

(a)   both balls are red,                        (b)   both balls are the same colour,

(c)   the balls are different colours,        (d)   at least one ball is yellow.

## Solution

The tree diagram below shows the probabilities and outcomes:

|  | 2nd Ball | OUTCOMES | PROBABILITIES |
|---|---|---|---|
| *1st Ball* | $\dfrac{6}{11}$ Y | Y Y | $\dfrac{7}{12} \times \dfrac{6}{11} = \dfrac{42}{132}$ |
| $\dfrac{7}{12}$ Y | $\dfrac{5}{11}$ R | Y R | $\dfrac{7}{12} \times \dfrac{5}{11} = \dfrac{35}{132}$ |
| $\dfrac{5}{12}$ R | $\dfrac{7}{11}$ Y | R Y | $\dfrac{5}{12} \times \dfrac{7}{11} = \dfrac{35}{132}$ |
|  | $\dfrac{4}{11}$ R | R R | $\dfrac{5}{12} \times \dfrac{4}{11} = \dfrac{20}{132}$ |

$$\text{total} = \dfrac{132}{132} = 1$$

(a)  $p(\text{both red}) = \dfrac{20}{132}$

$\qquad\qquad\qquad\quad = \dfrac{5}{33}$

(b)  $p(\text{both the same colour}) = p(\text{Y Y}) + p(\text{R R})$

$\qquad\qquad\qquad\qquad\qquad\quad = \dfrac{42}{132} + \dfrac{20}{132}$

$\qquad\qquad\qquad\qquad\qquad\quad = \dfrac{62}{132}$

$\qquad\qquad\qquad\qquad\qquad\quad = \dfrac{31}{66}$

(c)  $p(\text{different colours})$

$\qquad = 1 - p(\text{same colour}) \qquad$ or $\qquad p(\text{Y R}) + p(\text{R Y}) = \dfrac{35}{132} + \dfrac{35}{132}$

$\qquad = 1 - \dfrac{31}{66} \qquad\qquad\qquad\qquad\qquad\qquad\qquad\qquad = \dfrac{70}{132}$

$\qquad = \dfrac{35}{66} \qquad\qquad\qquad\qquad\qquad\qquad\qquad\qquad\quad = \dfrac{35}{66}$

(d)  $p(\text{at least one yellow})$

$\qquad = \dfrac{42}{132} + \dfrac{35}{132} + \dfrac{35}{132} \qquad\qquad$ or $\qquad\qquad = 1 - p(\text{R R})$

$\qquad = \dfrac{112}{132} \qquad\qquad\qquad\qquad\qquad\qquad\qquad\qquad = 1 - \dfrac{20}{132}$

$\qquad = \dfrac{28}{33} \qquad\qquad\qquad\qquad\qquad\qquad\qquad\qquad\quad = \dfrac{112}{132}$

$\qquad\qquad\qquad\qquad\qquad\qquad\qquad\qquad\qquad\qquad\quad = \dfrac{28}{33}$

## Example 2

There are 4 boys and 5 girls who are hoping to be selected for a school quiz team.
Two of them are selected at random to be in the team.

Determine the probability that:

(a)  2 boys are chosen,

(b)  at least 1 girl is chosen,

(c)  1 girl and 1 boy are chosen.

## Solution

The tree diagram below shows the outcomes and the probabilities:

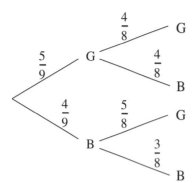

|  | OUTCOMES | PROBABILITIES |
|---|---|---|

$\frac{5}{9} \times \frac{4}{8} = \frac{20}{72} = \frac{5}{18}$

$\frac{5}{9} \times \frac{4}{8} = \frac{20}{72} = \frac{5}{18}$

$\frac{4}{9} \times \frac{5}{8} = \frac{20}{72} = \frac{5}{18}$

$\frac{4}{9} \times \frac{3}{8} = \frac{12}{72} = \frac{3}{18}$

total $= \frac{18}{18} = 1$

(a)  $p(2 \text{ boys}) = \frac{3}{18}$

$= \frac{1}{6}$

(b)  $p(\text{at least 1 girl}) = \frac{5}{18} + \frac{5}{18} + \frac{5}{18}$

$= \frac{15}{18}$

$= \frac{5}{6}$

(c)  $p(1 \text{ boy and 1 girl}) = \frac{5}{18} + \frac{5}{18}$

$= \frac{10}{18}$

$= \frac{5}{9}$

Note:  The questions in Examples 1 and 2 could have been answered *without* the use of tree diagrams, but a tree diagram helps greatly with the analysis of the problem; the same is true for the next example.

## Example 3

The probability that Ravi does his homework is $\frac{1}{10}$ if he goes out with his friends and $\frac{3}{5}$ of he does not go out with his friends.  The probability that Ravi goes out with his friends is $\frac{3}{4}$.  What is the probability that Ravi does his homework?

## Solution

*Solution 1*

$p\big((\text{goes out and does homework}) \text{ or } (\text{does not go out and does homework})\big)$

$=$

$p(\text{goes out}) \times p(\text{does homework}) + p(\text{does not go out}) \times p(\text{does homework})$

$= \quad \dfrac{3}{4} \times \dfrac{1}{10} \qquad\qquad + \qquad\qquad \dfrac{1}{4} \times \dfrac{3}{5}$

$= \quad \dfrac{3}{40} + \dfrac{3}{20}$

$= \quad \dfrac{9}{40}$

*Solution 2*

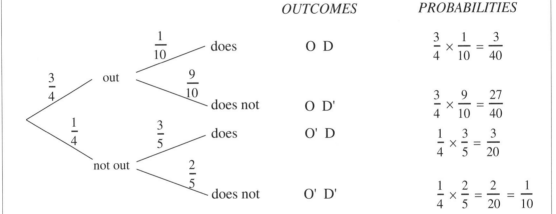

OUTCOMES        PROBABILITIES

O D        $\dfrac{3}{4} \times \dfrac{1}{10} = \dfrac{3}{40}$

O D'       $\dfrac{3}{4} \times \dfrac{9}{10} = \dfrac{27}{40}$

O' D       $\dfrac{1}{4} \times \dfrac{3}{5} = \dfrac{3}{20}$

O' D'      $\dfrac{1}{4} \times \dfrac{2}{5} = \dfrac{2}{20} = \dfrac{1}{10}$

Note: O' means *does not* go out, and D' means *does not* do homework.

$p(\text{does homework}) \; = \quad \dfrac{3}{40} + \dfrac{3}{20}$

$= \quad \dfrac{9}{40}$

## Exercises

1.    A bag contains 3 pink balls and 2 blue balls. One ball is taken out at random and not replaced. A second ball is then taken out.

   Determine the probability that:

   (a)   both balls are pink,

   (b)   both balls are the same colour,

   (c)   at least one ball is blue.

2.    In Tim's drawer there are 6 black socks and 5 white socks. He takes out two
      socks at random. What is the probability that he has taken two socks of the
      same colour?

3.    In a tennis club there are 5 boys and 3 girls in a training squad. Two are
      chosen at random to represent the club.
      Determine the probability that they are:
      (a)    both boys,

      (b)    both girls,

      (c)    a boy and a girl.

4.    Tara has five 10p coins and four 20p coins in her purse. She takes out two
      coins at random. What is the probability that she takes out at least 30p?

5.    There are 8 footballs in a store cupboard; one is yellow and the others are
      white. A pupil takes 2 footballs out of the cupboard at random. What is the
      probability that one of them is the yellow ball?

6.    The probability of Jeremy passing a maths exam is $\frac{2}{3}$ if he revises and $\frac{1}{3}$ if
      he does not revise. The probability that he revises is $\frac{1}{4}$. What is the
      probability of Jeremy passing the maths exam?

7.    The probability of Jenny getting to work on time is 0.8 if she gets up before
      7 a.m. and 0.4 if she does not get up before 7 a.m. The probability that
      Jenny gets up before 7 a.m. is 0.7. What is the probability that Jenny is *late*
      for work?

8.    Ian is an inept mountaineer who tends to fall from rock faces. The
      probability that he falls is 0.2 if the weather is dry but rises to 0.5 if it is
      wet. The probability of wet weather is 0.3. Determine the probability that
      Ian falls.

9.    A bag contains 7 blue counters, 5 green counters, 2 black counters and
      1 white counter. 3 counters are taken at random from the bag, without
      replacement. What is the probability that they are all the same colour?

10.   Peter and Jane play a game in which they each in turn take a counter at
      random from a bag containing 7 red counters and 3 yellow counters. The
      winner is the first to get a red counter. Jane goes first. By drawing a tree
      diagram, determine the probability that Peter wins the game.

# 11 | Angles, Bearings and Maps

## 11.1 | Angle Measures

In this section we review measuring angles, and the different types of angles.

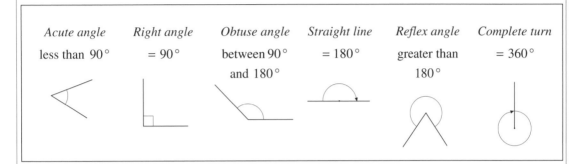

| Acute angle | Right angle | Obtuse angle | Straight line | Reflex angle | Complete turn |
|---|---|---|---|---|---|
| less than $90°$ | $= 90°$ | between $90°$ and $180°$ | $= 180°$ | greater than $180°$ | $= 360°$ |

### Example 1

Measure the angle in the diagram.

### Solution

Using a protractor, the angle can be measured as $35°$.

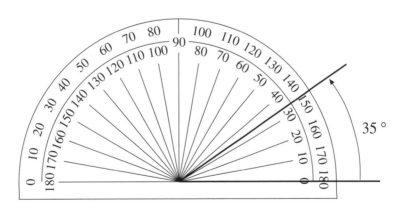

$35°$

### Example 2

State whether each of the angles below is *acute, obtuse* or *reflex*.

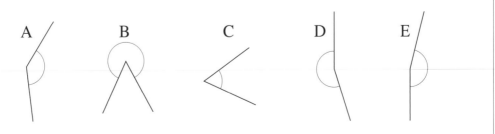

A    B    C    D    E

## Solution

A   *Obtuse* as it is between 90 ° and 180 °.

B   *Reflex* as it is greater than 180 °.

C   *Acute* as it is less than 90 °

D   *Reflex* as it is greater than 180 °.

E   *Obtuse* as it is between 90 ° and 180 °.

## Exercises

1.   Measure the following angles:

(a)

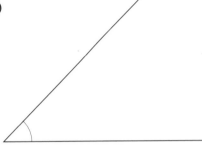

(b)

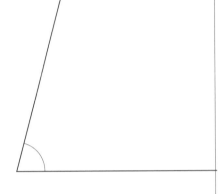

(c)

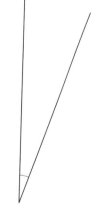

(d)

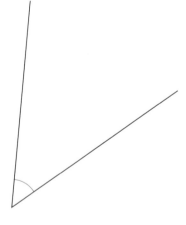

2.   Measure the following angles:

(a)                                         (b)

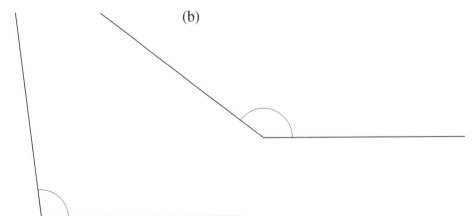

(c) 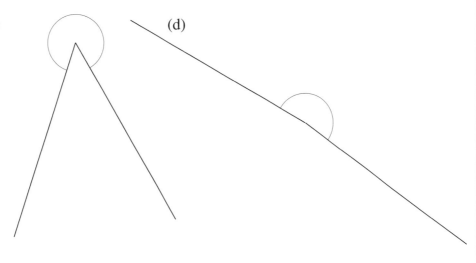 (d)

(e) 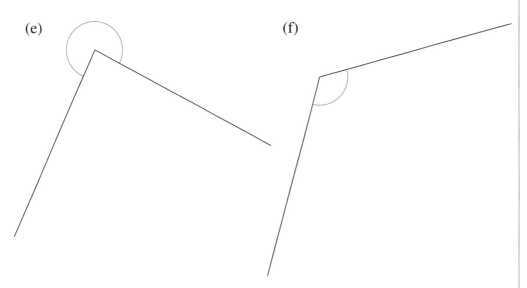 (f)

3. State whether each of the following angles is *acute, obtuse* or *reflex*.

(a)  (b)  (c)

(d)  (e)  (f)

4.   (a)   Measure the angles in the triangle below:

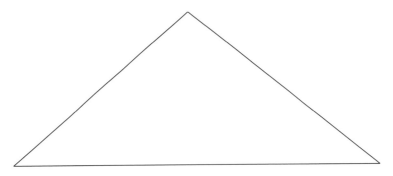

(b)   What is the sum of the three angles?

5.   (a)   Measure the angles in the quadrilateral
          opposite:

(b)   What is the sum of the four angles?

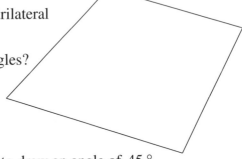

6.   (a)   Without using a protractor, try to draw an angle of $45°$.

(b)   Measure your angle to see how accurate you were.

7.   (a)   Draw the angle shown in the diagram.

(b)   Measure the acute angle that you also draw.

(c)   Check that the two angles add up to $360°$.

280°

8.   (a)   Measure the three angles marked
          in the diagram.

(b)   Check that they add up to $360°$.

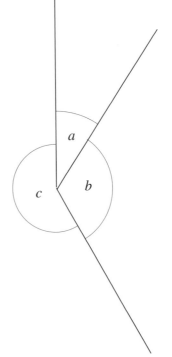

9.  (a)  Measure the two angles in
        the diagram.

    (b)  Check that they add up to 180 °.

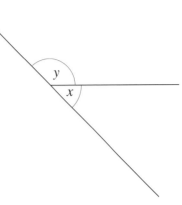

10.  (a)  Without using a protractor, try to draw an angle of 300 °.

    (b)  Check your answer by measuring the angle with a protractor.

# 11.2  Parallel and Intersecting Lines

When a line *intersects* (or crosses) a pair
of parallel lines, there are some simple
rules that can be used to calculate
unknown angles.

The arrows on the lines indicate that they
are parallel.

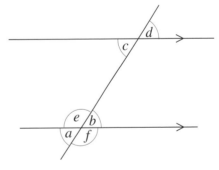

$a = b$ $\left(\text{and } c = d, \text{ and } e = f\right)$     These are called *vertically opposite* angles.

$a = c$ $\left(\text{and } b = d\right)$     These are called *corresponding* angles.

$b = c$     These are called *alternate* angles.

$a + e = 180$ °, because adjacent angles on a straight line add up to 180 °.
                These are called *supplementary* angles.

Note also, that  $c + e = 180$ °  (*allied* or *supplementary* angles)

## Example 1

In the diagram opposite, find the unknown
angles if $a = 150\,°$.

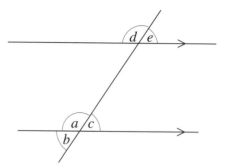

## Solution

To find $b$:

$$a + b = 180\,°$$ (angles on a straight line, supplementary angles)

$$150\,° + b = 180\,°$$

$$b = 30\,°$$

To find $c$:

$$c = b$$ (vertically opposite angles *or* angles on a straight line)

$$c = 30\,°$$

To find $d$:

$$d = a$$ (corresponding angles)

$$d = 150\,°$$

To find $e$:

$$e = c$$ (corresponding angles)

$$e = 30\,°$$

## Example 2

Find the size of the unknown angles in
the parallelogram shown in this diagram:

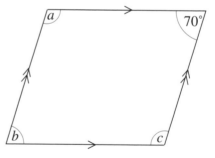

## Solution

To find $a$:

$$a + 70\,° = 180\,°$$ (allied *or* supplementary angles)

$$a = 110\,°$$

To find $b$:

$$b + a = 180\,°$$ (allied *or* supplementary angles)

$$b + 110\,° = 180\,°$$

$$b = 70\,°$$

To find $c$:

$c + 70° = 180°$        (allied  *or*  supplementary angles)

$c = 110°$

*or*

$c = 360° - (a + b + 70°)$        (angle sum of a quadrilateral)

$= 360° - 250°$

$= 110°$

*or*

$c = a$        (opposite angles of a parallelogram are equal)

# Exercises

1. Which angles in the diagram are the same size as:

    (a) $a$,

    (b) $b$ ?

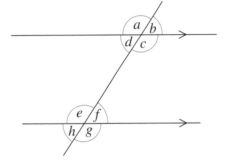

2. Find the size of each of the angles marked with letters in the diagrams below, giving reasons for your answers:

    (a)

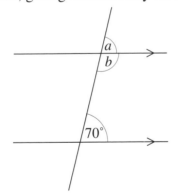

    (b)

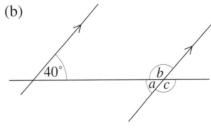

    (c)

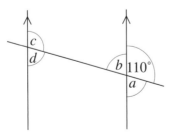

    (d)

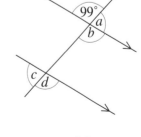

3. Find the size of the three unknown angles in the parallelogram opposite:

4. One angle in a parallelogram measures 36°. What is the size of each of the other three angles?

5. One angle in a rhombus measures 133°. What is the size of each of the other three angles?

6. Find the sizes of the unknown angles marked with letters in the diagram:

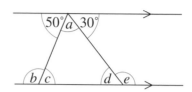

7. (a) In the diagram opposite, find the sizes of the angles marked in the triangle. Give reasons for your answers.

   (b) What special name is given to the triangle in the diagram?

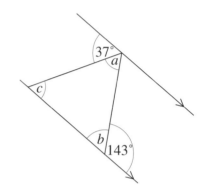

8. The diagram shows a bicycle frame. Find the sizes of the unknown angles *a, b* and *c*.

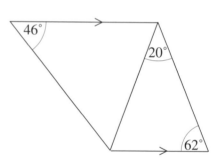

9.

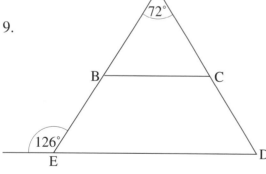

   BCDE is a trapezium.

   (a) Find the sizes of all the unknown angles, giving reasons for your answers.

   (b) What is the special name given to this type of trapezium?

# 11.3 Bearings

Bearings are a measure of direction, with north taken as a reference. If you are travelling north, your bearing is 000 °.

If you walk from O in the direction shown in the diagram, you are walking on a bearing of 110 °.

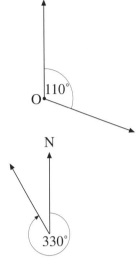

Bearings are always measured *clockwise from north*, and are given as three figures, for example:

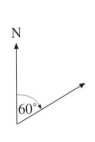

Bearing 060 °

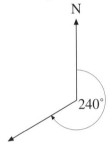

Bearing 240 °

Bearing 330 °

## Example 1

On what bearing is a ship sailing if it is heading:

(a)   E,

(b)   S,

(c)   W,

(d)   SE,

(e)   NW ?

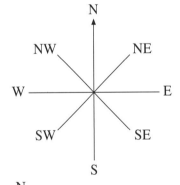

## Solution

(a)

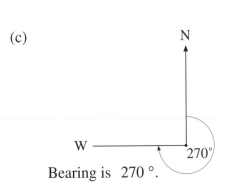

Bearing is 090 °.

(b)

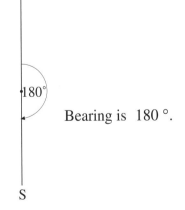

Bearing is 180 °.

(c)

Bearing is 270 °.

(d)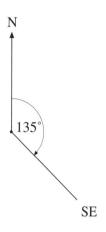

Bearing is  135 °

(e)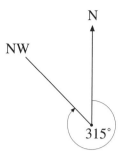

Bearing is  315 °

 Example 2

A ship sails from A to B on a bearing of  060 °.  On what bearing must it sail if it is to return from B to A?

 **Solution**

The diagram shows the journey from A to B.

Extending the line of the journey allows an angle of 60 ° to be marked at B.

Bearing of A from B  =  60 ° + 180 °

=  240 °

and this is called a *back bearing* or a *reciprocal bearing*.

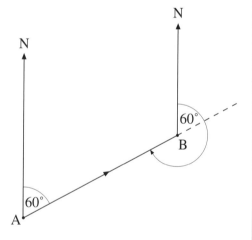

 Exercises

1.     What angle do you turn through  if you turn clockwise from:

(a)    N  to  S,                          (b)    E  to  W,

(c)    N  to  NE,                        (d)    N  to  SW,

(e)    W  to  NW ?

2.     Copy and complete the table:

| Direction | Bearing |
|---|---|
| N | |
| NE | |
| W | |
| SW | |